BIOLOGY
Science for Life
Laboratory Manual

INSTRUCTOR'S EDITION
SECOND EDITION

Virginia Borden • Colleen Belk
UNIVERSITY OF MINNESOTA – DULUTH

PEARSON
Prentice
Hall

Upper Saddle River, NJ 07458

Editor-in-Chief, Science: Dan Kaveney
Executive Editor: Teresa Ryu Chung
Senior Media Editor: Patrick Shriner
Assistant Editor: Andrew Sobel
Editorial Assistant: Gina Kayed
Executive Managing Editor: Kathleen Schiaparelli
Assistant Managing Editor: Karen Bosch
Production Editor: Donna King, PPA
Supplement Cover Manager: Paul Gourhan
Supplement Cover Designer: Christopher Kossa
Manufacturing Buyer: Ilene Kahn
Manufacturing Manager: Alexis Heydt-Long

© 2007 Pearson Education, Inc.
Pearson Prentice Hall
Pearson Education, Inc.
Upper Saddle River, NJ 07458

All rights reserved. No part of this book may be reproduced in any form or by any means, without permission in writing from the publisher.

Pearson Prentice Hall™ is a trademark of Pearson Education, Inc.

The author and publisher of this book have used their best efforts in preparing this book. These efforts include the development, research, and testing of the theories and programs to determine their effectiveness. The author and publisher make no warranty of any kind, expressed or implied, with regard to these programs or the documentation contained in this book. The author and publisher shall not be liable in any event for incidental or consequential damages in connection with, or arising out of, the furnishing, performance, or use of these programs.

This work is protected by United States copyright laws and is provided solely for the use of instructors in teaching their courses and assessing student learning. Dissemination or sale of any part of this work (including on the World Wide Web) will destroy the integrity of the work and is not permitted. The work and materials from it should never be made available to students except by instructors using the accompanying text in their classes. All recipients of this work are expected to abide by these restrictions and to honor the intended pedagogical purposes and the needs of other instructors who rely on these materials.

Printed in the United States of America

10 9 8 7 6 5 4 3 2 1

ISBN 0-13-173373-7

Pearson Education Ltd., *London*
Pearson Education Australia Pty. Ltd., *Sydney*
Pearson Education Singapore, Pte. Ltd.
Pearson Education North Asia Ltd., *Hong Kong*
Pearson Education Canada, Inc., *Toronto*
Pearson Educación de Mexico, S.A. de C.V.
Pearson Education—Japan, *Tokyo*
Pearson Education Malaysia, Pte. Ltd.

Table of Contents

Preface to the Instructor's Edition

The *Biology: Science for Life Laboratory Manual* is designed to complement the textbook *Biology: Science for Life*. As with the textbook, the lab manual actively engages students and develops their scientific literacy and critical thinking skills. The seventeen topics in the manual are closely tied to the chapters of the textbook. In addition, because the same authors wrote both texts, the coordination between the lecture and laboratory can be nearly seamless.

The elements that distinguish the textbook are repeated and extended in the lab manual. As in the text, the lab manual:

Demonstrates science as a process. Each topic contains one or more exercises on hypothesis testing and evaluation of results. Throughout their use of the manual, students' critical thinking skills are developed as they learn to appreciate the explanatory strength of the scientific method. In addition, because many of the hypothesis tests in the manual are open-ended and do not produce "canned" results, students will understand the challenges of science and begin to see the dynamic nature of biologists' search for an understanding of the natural world.

Engages students through analogies and models. Most labs contain exercises that describe complex biological processes using simple and familiar items. These analogies will allow you to focus on the essential processes you need to understand without getting bogged down in the more technical details of the process. Many of these exercises are followed up by a more traditional lab activity. By learning via analogy first, students are better able to appreciate the meaning and usefulness of the more traditional activities.

Relates science to everyday topics. As in the textbook, each lab topic is connected to additional topics that have both scientific and social aspects. Incorporating larger societal questions into the laboratory setting allows students to appreciate the usefulness of science to everyday life, and also serves to humanize both the process of science and its practitioners. In large classes, laboratory sections can be the best places for substantive student discussion—and consequently, substantive learning.

Additional Features of the Instructor's Edition

The instructor's manual is designed to maximize the teaching value of the laboratory manual and simplify the instructor's preparation. The Instructor's Edition:

Provides pre-laboratory quiz questions. Each lab topic is introduced with a pre-laboratory reading segment. Quiz questions in Appendix A of the Instructor's Edition provide a straightforward way to review the key concepts of the upcoming lab at the beginning of a lab period and may also serve as incentive to encourage student preparation before labs.

Integrates materials and methods into lab exercises.   Each lab exercise is published in its entirety in the Instructor's Edition, with relevant materials listed at the beginning of the exercise and descriptions of methods incorporated into key steps. This simplifies the instructor's preparation by providing all necessary information for set up and execution of the exercises in the same place.

Offers pedagogical notes.   We have used these lab exercises in our own classes over many semesters and have developed effective teaching strategies in order to get the most out of the exercise and the students. Many of these time-tested strategies are included in the Instructor's Edition.

Includes sample data and answers to student manual questions.   Many of the exercises require students to collect and analyze data. Where warranted, example results and key answer points to printed questions are included in the Instructor's Edition.

We are proud to be a part of the community of Biology instructors and know that this community is made up of very talented, highly creative, and dedicated teachers. We look forward to learning about how you have used the *Biology: Science for Life Laboratory Manual* and hearing your suggestions for changes and improvements.

We are thankful for our excellent editor, Andrew Sobel, whose support and careful work during the production of the Second Edition of this manual were invaluable. Sincere thanks also go out to Donna King and Karen Bosch, who skillfully coordinated the entire production process. Most importantly, we owe a debt of thanks to our reviewers, listed below. This lab manual has been much improved by their critical review and excellent suggestions. We are extremely grateful for their efforts.

Sylvester Allred	Northern Arizona University
Lynne Arneson	American University
Donna Becker	Northern Michigan University
Lawrence Bradford	Benedictine College
David Byres	Florida Community College – Jacksonville
Danette Carlton	Virginia State University
William Coleman	University of Hartford
Heather DeHart	Western Kentucky University
Elizabeth A. Desy	Southwest Minnesota State University
William J. Edwards	Niagara University
Anne Galbraith	University of Wisconsin – La Crosse
Tony J. Greenfield	Southwest Minnesota State University
Andrew Goyke	Northland College
Julie Hens	University of Maryland University College
Leland N. Holland	Pasco Hernando Community College
Hetty B. Jones	Savannah State University
Michelle Mabry	Davis and Elkins College
Ken Marr	Green River Community College
Monica McGee	University of North Carolina – Wilmington
Elizabeth McPartlan	De Anza College
John McWilliams	Oklahoma Baptist University
Diane Melroy	University of North Carolina – Wilmington
Marjorie B. Miller	Greenville Technical College
James Munger	Boise State University
Greg Pryor	University of Florida
Pele Eve Rich	Mt. San Jacinto College
Susan Rohde	Triton College
John Richard Schrock	Emporia State University

Joanne Russell	Manchester Community College
Julie Schroer	Bismarck State College
Douglas Smith	Clarion University of Pennsylvania
Carol St. Angelo	Hofstra University
Janet Vigna	Grand Valley State University
James A. Wallis	St. Petersburg College
Lisa Weasel	Portland State University
Richard Whitkus	Sonoma State University
Judy Williams	Southeastern Oklahoma State University
Danette Young	Virginia State University

Virginia Borden and Colleen Belk

Topic Correspondence Grid

Lab Manual Topic...	...corresponds to Second Edition text chapter (sections)
1	1 (all)
2	2 (all), 3 (3.3), 4 (4.3)
3	3 (3.1, 3.2, 3.4), 4 (4.2)
4	5 (5.1, 5.3, 5.4, 5.5)
5	5 (5.6), 6 (6.1, 6.2), 7 (7.1)
6	5 (5.2), 7 (7.4)
7	8 (all)
8	9 (9.1, 9.3)
9	10 (all)
10	11 (all)
11	12 (all)
12	13 (all), 14 (14.2)
13	14 (14.2, 14.3)
14	19 (all)
15	20 (all)
16	21 (all)
17	22 (22.1, 22.2), 23 (23.1)

The Scientific Method

Learning Objectives

A pre-laboratory quiz is available in Appendix A on page 197.

1. Describe science as a process of proposing and testing hypotheses.
2. Distinguish between statements that are testable by science and those that are not.
3. Describe the meaning and purpose of experimental controls.
4. Design an experiment to test a hypothesis.
5. Define "statistical significance" and describe what statistics describing an experimental result can and cannot tell us about the hypothesis.
6. Distinguish between "statistical significance" and "practical significance."

Pre-laboratory Reading

The word "science" is derived from a Latin verb *scientia*, meaning "to know." Science is a way of knowing about the world. There are many other ways of knowing—in other words, of finding truth—including faith, philosophy, and cultural tradition. All of these ways of knowing help us understand different aspects of our world.

The essence of science as a way of knowing is the formulation and testing of statements called **hypotheses**. A hypothesis is a tentative explanation of how something works or of the cause of an event. Scientific hypotheses must be testable. In other words, hypotheses must be formulated in such a way that unambiguous observations of the natural world can help us support or reject them. Hypotheses are tested via **objective** observations; that is, observations that when made by many different, independent people would produce the same results.

Many cleansing products on the market today advertise that they "kill germs" or, more specifically, that they are "antibacterial." This label typically indicates that these products contain triclosan or another related antiseptic chemical. Consumers concerned about food poisoning or other bacteria-caused illnesses preferentially purchase these products based on their assumption that the following hypothesis is true:

Antibacterial soap kills more bacteria on hands than standard hand soap.

Good scientists are usually skeptical of untested hypotheses. For instance, there are reasons to doubt the hypothesis that antibacterial soap is a more effective cleanser. The action of hand washing *physically* removes bacteria from hands. It is not clear that the chemical composition of the soap (outside of the fats, oils, and alkali that all soaps contain) is an important factor in disinfecting hands. Without testing the hypothesis, there is no way to determine whether it is correct.

The first step in testing a hypothesis is making a **prediction** about the observations one would expect to make if the hypothesis was correct. You can think of a prediction as the "then" part of an "If … then …" statement. In other words, "If this hypothesis is true, then I expect to observe…." A prediction forms the basis for evaluating the truth of any statement. The prediction of the hypothesis that antibacterial soap kills more bacteria on hands than standard hand soap is that *hands washed with antibacterial soap will have fewer bacteria on them than hands washed with standard soap.* Many (but not all) scientific hypotheses can be tested through experimentation. An **experiment** is a contrived situation set up by a researcher solely for the purpose of testing a hypothesis. The hypothesis about antibacterial soap is testable by experiment.

When a hypothesis can be tested through experimentation, the most effective way to remove ambiguity from the results is to design a controlled experiment. **Control** indicates that the researcher works to ensure that all subjects in the experiment are treated identically (except for the experimental treatment). In other words, a control helps to verify that the effect of an experimental treatment is due to the treatment itself and not another factor. One common control in an experiment is to keep both the subjects and the technicians performing the experiment unaware of which individuals are receiving the experimental treatment and which are not. Experiments designed in this manner are called **double blind**, because the participants cannot "see" what outcome is expected and, even unconsciously, bias the results.

Measurements collected from tests of hypotheses are called **data**. Data collected from experimental and control groups are summarized and compared using the tool of **statistics**. Statistics is a specialized branch of mathematics designed to help scientists relate the results of a limited experiment to a larger population. Individuals in an experiment make up a **sample** of the population they are derived from. A sample is always an imperfect reflection of the whole population. As a result, there are two reasons that experimental and control samples may differ: (1) the experimental treatment has a real effect; or (2) by chance, individuals selected for the experimental group are quite different than the individuals selected for the control group. If a statistical test indicates that there is a very low likelihood that (2) is true, the results of an experiment are termed **statistically significant**.

(15 Minutes)

Instructors: The lab as written is designed to be completed over the course of two class periods—the bulk in the first week, and the remainder as the first part of the following lab section. If you want to make this a single-section exercise, you have a couple of options:

1. *Allow the students to work through the first parts of the lab, formulating a prediction and coming up with the experimental design. Then, you can provide them with data—either data you generated in a previous semester of the course, data you "made up," or you can contact the lab manual authors for data from their students—for the analysis part of the lab. You might want to have the students actually perform the experiment, collecting the data in the next lab session to provide to the following semester's (or year's) class.*

2. *You can replace this hypothesis test with another from the lab manual. This will take some modification of the directions in the manual (you will probably need to create an additional handout), but many of the steps will be the same.*

The first several lab exercises are discussions. There are several techniques for maximizing the effectiveness of these discussions:

1. *Set a time limit for when the discussion is to be completed and circulate throughout the laboratory listening in and asking leading questions of students to keep them on task.*

LAB EXERCISE 1.1

Practice Identifying and Creating Scientifically Testable Hypotheses

A. Review these statements with your laboratory partners and be prepared to share your answers with your laboratory instructor and/or other students.

B. For each statement, determine whether it is a scientific hypothesis as written, and if not, why not.

C. If the statement is not a scientific hypothesis, try to modify the statement so that it is testable.

D. Are any hypotheses impossible to test objectively?

1. It is wrong to perform medically unnecessary cosmetic surgery.

   This statement is not scientific because it is an opinion. There is no way to test this statement objectively because not all observers can agree upon which activities are "right" or "wrong."

2. Biology lab is more fun than a barrel of monkeys.

   This statement is not scientific as stated because it is an opinion and cannot be objectively evaluated. However, we could objectively test a similar hypothesis stated as "On average, people rate participating in biology lab as more enjoyable than observing a barrel of monkeys."

3. God created Earth and all living creatures.

   This statement is not scientific because it involves a supernatural entity—God. Supernatural entities or forces do not conform to the laws of nature and cannot be objectively observed. This statement cannot be modified into a scientific hypothesis.

4. Plants that are spoken to regularly grow more rapidly than plants that are not spoken to.

   This statement is a scientific hypothesis.

5. Women are more intelligent than men.

   Because observers will disagree on what behaviors or skills denote greater "intelligence," this statement is not a scientific hypothesis (it cannot be objectively tested). However, a statement such as "Women have higher IQ scores than men" can be objectively tested because IQ exams are a quantifiable measure.

2. *Keep each discussion separate; in other words, ask the students to work on the first discussion and then bring the group back together to share their answers before asking them to move to the second discussion.*

3. *Alternatively, ask students to write answers in the lab manual and have them turn these in for credit.*

LAB EXERCISE 1.2

Preparing to Design an Experiment

(15 Minutes)

In the introduction to the lab, we put forth the following scientific hypothesis:

Antibacterial soap kills more bacteria on hands than standard hand soap.

A. Discuss the following questions with your lab partners and be prepared to share your answers with the lab instructor and other students.

1. What objective measures could we use to test the hypothesis about the cleansing power of antibacterial soap?

   A count of the amount of bacteria found on hands washed with antibacterial soap versus standard soap.

2. If the hypothesis is correct, what would you predict the outcome of the test to be?

   There will be more bacteria on hands washed with standard soap than with antibacterial soap.

3. To test this hypothesis, we could simply survey everyone in lab regarding his or her use of this soap. Presumably, at least some of the class almost always uses antibacterial hand soap and some almost never use this type of soap. After we found these two classes of people, we could simply compare the number of bacteria found on their hands. Why is this a poor test of the hypothesis?

   It is inadequately controlled. In other words, there might be differences between individuals who use antibacterial soap and those who do not that would also influence how much bacteria they have on their hands. For instance, someone who uses antibacterial soap might be more aware, or more concerned, about exposure to bacteria and thus might wash their hands more often during the day. If this is the case, and if hand washing itself is the most effective way to remove bacteria, then people who use antibacterial soap will have fewer bacteria on their hands, but not because they use this particular type of soap.

4. We could test the hypothesis by designating half the class as "antibacterial soapers" and the other half as "regular soapers," having everyone wash their hands with the soap they have been assigned to, and then comparing the number of bacteria found on the hands of members of each group. However, this approach also is flawed. Why?

   It is inadequately controlled in that the two groups in the experiment are not being treated identically except for the soap they use. Members of each group have been told something different about the soap they are using; especially if they know that the experiment is testing the effectiveness of antibacterial soap, this could influence how careful they are when they wash their hands. In other words, the experimental design is not "double blind."

Materials:

- *Liquid hand soap: one containing triclosan and a similar formula soap minus triclosan (One 8-ounce container is more than enough for our class of 200 students in 9 labs.) Soft-soap brand soaps that are identical in appearance and nearly identical in formula except for presence/absence of triclosan can be found in most major grocery stores.*
- *Petri dishes filled with nutrient agar (two per student)*
- *Sterile cotton swabs for transferring bacteria from hands to petri dishes (2 per student)*
- *Test tubes of sterile water (if students will be swabbing dirty hands)*
- *Permanent markers (1 per student group)*

Instructors: If students will not return to lab for several days, transfer the Petri dishes to a cold room or refrigerator after 24 or 48 hours.

Instructors: The intent here is to have students actively engaged in setting up the experimental protocol. As with the other discussions, an effective technique to keep everyone on task is to circulate among the lab groups, asking leading questions and answering any question they may have.

The experimental protocol is somewhat flexible, although it is strongly advisable to come up with a design that is blind and with a standard hand washing and "bacteria transferring" technique that all participants use. It can also be useful to measure bacteria levels on all participants' hands before washing with soap. Additionally, if you intend to pool data from various lab sections, it will be up to the individual laboratory instructors to gently "guide" each section toward a common protocol. We prefer to allow each lab to design their own protocol; although we lose statistical power, this approach seems to be more satisfying to the students.

L A B   E X E R C I S E   1 . 3

Design and Perform a Controlled Experiment

The last discussion exercise should have led you to consider some of the factors you will need to control when testing the hypothesis that antibacterial soap kills more bacteria on hands than standard hand soap. Now you should be prepared to design a well-controlled experiment to test this hypothesis.

First, you will need a short primer on how bacteria levels can be counted.

- Bacteria are single-celled organisms that are much too small to be seen with the naked eye, and many can only be seen under the highest magnification of a typical light microscope.
- Bacteria reproduce rapidly when in contact with a nutrient source.
- If an individual bacterial cell is transferred to a gel-like nutrient source, the cell will multiply into millions of descendants, producing a colony of cells that is visible to the naked eye. A bacterial colony that arose from a single cell typically appears as a distinct circular dot on the surface of the agar.
- Thus, the number of bacteria on a given surface can be estimated by transferring those bacteria to a petri dish filled with nutrient agar gel, giving those cells 24–48 hours to multiply, and then counting the number of visible colonies on the plate.

A. Work with your lab partners to design a controlled experimental test of the hypothesis.

   Materials available:

   - Liquid hand soap: one containing triclosan and a similar formula soap minus triclosan (Note: most of these soaps instruct users to rub the lather on their hands for 30 seconds to get the maximum effect.)
   - Petri dishes filled with nutrient agar (two per student)
   - Sterile cotton swabs for transferring bacteria from hands to petri dishes
   - Sterile water to swab dirty hands with
   - Permanent markers

B. Write an outline of your experiment below. Be prepared to share this design with the lab instructor and/or your classmates.

Soap can be transferred to unlabeled dispenser bottles that are designated "soap X" and "soap Y" to facilitate blinding. It might be impossible for the instructor to be blinded as well, but because students will be washing their own hands, transferring bacteria to plates and counting colonies by themselves, this is much less crucial.

Damp hands allow the transfer of more bacterial cells than dry hands. If the class will be doing a before/after comparison, students should wet their hands, transfer bacteria, wash with soap and rinse, and then transfer bacteria again.

Bacteria can be transferred to the agar gel either by students touching the gel directly (standardize the digits and amount of skin that is touching the plate) or by swabbing the dampened hands with a cotton swab and then sweeping it across the surface of the agar (standardizing the hand surfaces that are swabbed).

C. When you have finished, your lab instructor will lead a discussion that will generate a class protocol based on the common and best elements of each plan.

D. Follow the class protocol to perform an experimental test of the hypothesis. Results will be available in the next class period.

LAB EXERCISE 1.4

Collect Experimental Results

(25 Minutes)

Materials:
- *Computer with Excel installed*
- *Hand calculators (optional) — up to 1 per student, but can be shared*

A. Count the number of bacterial colonies on your agar plate and record them here:
- Before washing _____
- After washing _____

Instructors: The Excel spreadsheet should contain the three right-most columns of the following table. At the bottom of each column, you can type in the formula for calculating the average in one row [= average(number range)] and the formula for calculating 95% confidence interval in the following row [= confidence(.05, (stdev(number range)],(count(number range))].

B. What was your treatment group? _____

C. Input your data into the Excel spreadsheet provided by the instructor.

D. Fill in Table 1.1, summarizing all of the data collected by the class. Recall that the number of colonies on the plates is approximately equivalent to the number of bacteria initially transferred.

TABLE 1.1

Student	Bacteria Transferred Before Washing	Bacteria Transferred After Washing with Soap X, OR…	Bacteria Transferred After Washing with Soap Y
Total number of colonies (add up all of the numbers in each row)			
Count (number of values you added to get the result above)			
Average number of colonies (Divide the total number of colonies by the count)			

LAB EXERCISE 1.5   *(20 Minutes)*

Summarize Experimental Results

A. Calculate the average number of colonies in each treatment group by summing all values in a column and dividing by the number of students in each treatment group. (See Table 1.1.)

- Before _____
- Group X_____
- Group Y _____

B. Ask your lab instructor which soap was antibacterial and which was standard.

- Soap X _____
- Soap Y _____

C. Fill in Table 1.2, using the confidence interval data generated by your lab instructor.

Instructors: This provides students some experience working with data and calculating averages. However, this number has already been generated on the Excel spreadsheet, so the step is not necessary and may be skipped if time requires.

TABLE 1.2

	Before Treatment	**Washed with Antibacterial Soap**	**Washed with Standard Soap**
Average number of colonies per plate			
95% confidence value (available from the Excel spreadsheet)			
Range of values (the lowest and highest values in the data set)			

D. Create a box-and-whiskers graph to summarize the data in the preceding table by using the template in Figure 1.1.

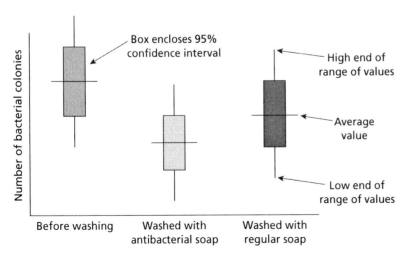

FIGURE 1.1

• The "95% confidence interval" is a measure of the variability of the data. It is essentially the range of values that has a 95% chance of containing the "true" population mean (in other words, the average number of bacteria found if we had performed this experiment with the entire human population as our sample). The mean *minus* the 95% confidence value is the low end of this range, and the mean *plus* the 95% confidence value is the high end of this range. The true population mean has a 95% likelihood of being within the box on the graph.

LAB EXERCISE 1.6

Evaluate Results

A number of statistical formulas exist that would allow us to test whether the difference between the number of bacterial colonies produced by the two different hand-washing treatments is statistically significant. However, to avoid delving into a complicated discussion of statistics, we can use the visual representation of the data in the graph that you just generated to determine whether the results are likely to show a significant difference.

In general, *if the confidence interval for either sample mean overlaps with the other sample mean, the average difference between the two sample means is not significant.* If this is the case, there is a more than 5% chance that the true population means of the two treatments are identical. The "5% chance" that the treatment had no effect is the standard value used by scientists to determine whether a difference between two samples is significant. In contrast, if there is no overlap between the confidence intervals, the result is likely to be significant.

In simpler terms:

IF the results are **not significant**

THEN there is a **greater than 5% chance** that the treatment has no effect, or that the two treatments are identical.

IF the results are **significant**

THEN there is a **5% or less chance** that the treatment has no effect, or that the two treatments are identical.

In addition, the box-and-whiskers graph conveys other information:

• If the confidence interval boxes are large, the sample was extremely variable. This could indicate that a larger sample size is required to observe any effect of the experimental treatment.
• If the overlap between the confidence interval of one sample and the mean of another sample is relatively small, this suggests a difference between the two treatments. However, the results still do not allow us to reject the hypothesis.

A. Discuss the following questions with your lab partners and be prepared to share with your lab instructor and/or classmates.

   1. Examine the box-and-whiskers graph produced by the data. What does it tell you about the hypothesis that antibacterial soap kills more bacteria on hands than regular soap?

   Students' answers to this question will depend on the actual data generated. Experience with this method of testing the hypothesis indicates that the results are often variable and inconclusive. This type of result actually generates more discussion than a clearer positive result.

2. Do you think that to get a clearer view of the status of the hypothesis, the experiment should be repeated with a larger sample size? Why or why not?

In general, the answer to this question is yes, because lab sections are typically small and the number of individuals in each treatment group is also small, leading to very large confidence intervals. Including more subjects in the experiment would help avoid the problem of a single outlier skewing the results.

LAB EXERCISE 1.7   (10 Minutes)

Discuss the Distinction Between Statistical Significance and Practical Significance

A statistically significant result does not necessarily tell us whether the results of the experiment indicate anything of practical value. For instance, a statistically significant but *small* difference between the number of bacteria on hands washed with antibacterial soap and hands washed with standard soap may have no effect on how healthy soap users are.

A. Discuss the following questions with your lab partners and be prepared to share your answers with the lab instructor and/or your classmates:

1. A drug that may soon become available to consumers has the following characteristics: It reduces the length of common cold symptoms (for most varieties of common cold) from 7.3 days to 6.3 days. Individuals who used the drug used 25% fewer tissues than people in the control group and had 33% fewer nights with disrupted sleep. These differences between the two groups are all statistically significant. What additional information about this drug, and what factors in your life, would influence whether these significant results were practically significant to you?

Students might want to know how expensive the drug will be to consumers and what additional side effects it causes. Their decision about whether to use it depends on the answers to these questions, the number of colds they suffer and how disruptive these colds are, among other factors.

2. Sometimes, experimental results are statistically significant, but critics will argue that these results are an inconclusive test of the hypothesis. For instance, in a test of the hypothesis that regular aspirin consumption reduces the risk of heart attack, white male volunteers who took a single regular-strength aspirin each day had a 50% lower risk of heart attack than white males who did not take aspirin. Why would women and African American men argue that this hypothesis requires further testing?

Biological and social differences between women and men and between whites and blacks might mean that the results of this hypothesis test do not apply to these other populations.

TOPIC 1
_____

POST-LABORATORY QUIZ

THE SCIENTIFIC METHOD

1. Describe two characteristics that define a hypothesis as "scientific."

2. A hypothesis can be scientific and logical, but that does not mean it is true. To determine whether a hypothesis should be accepted as correct, it must be _____ .

3. A recent experiment indicated that hormone replacement therapy in women increases the risk of suffering Alzheimer's disease. Hormone therapy is provided to women in pills containing estrogen and progesterone. What would be an appropriate control group for this experiment?

4. Scientists are interested in the following hypothesis: Exposure to bacteria and waste products present in and on farm and pet animals in early childhood reduces the risk of the child developing asthma or severe allergies. Describe a prediction of this hypothesis.

5. Define "double blind" in the context of an experiment.

6. Describe how you could experimentally test the hypothesis that ingesting the herb *Ginkgo biloba* improves memory. Be sure to include a description of the experimental control.

7. A relatively small group of individuals that is meant to be representative of a larger population is termed a _____ of that population.

8. A statistically significant difference between two samples is defined as one that has a _____ chance or less of occurring if the populations the two samples came from are not different.

9. What does a statistically significant result in an experiment comparing an experimental group to a control group mean?

That the two groups are different enough from each other that you can assume that the experimental treatment has an effect.

10. The risk of premature death is 20% higher in smokers compared to nonsmokers. This difference is statistically significant and widely known. Using the idea of statistical versus practical significance, explain why so many people continue to smoke.

Smokers perceive immediate benefits to smoking: for some, the nicotine in the cigarettes is a welcome stimulant; for others, smoking serves as an appetite suppressant. These benefits are weighed by smokers against the increased risk of death that smoking carries. In their minds, the practical significance of a 20% increase in risk of early death is low relative to the practical significance of the immediate benefits of smoking.

TOPIC 2
Cells and Energy

Learning Objectives

1. Define the characteristics of life.
2. Examine characteristics of prokaryotic and eukaryotic cells.
3. Understand the concept of homeostasis.
4. Examine the role of the cell membrane in maintaining homeostasis.
5. Explore the process of photosynthesis as the major source of biological energy.

A pre-laboratory quiz is available in Appendix A on page 199.

Pre-laboratory Reading

Biology is the study ("*logy*") of life ("*bio*"). However, it is surprisingly difficult to define "life"—while it is easy to see that a dog is alive, what about a mushroom or a cactus? And what about a virus, which requires infecting another organism in order to reproduce? Defining life is not just an academic exercise; determining the criteria for the existence of life informs the search for life on other planets, the abortion debate, and discussions of the appropriate use of stem cells, among other topics.

All living organisms are made up of cells. Cells are generally divided into two major categories: those that contain a nucleus, which houses their DNA, are known as **eukaryotes** (meaning "true kernel"), whereas those without a nucleus are called **prokaryotes** (meaning "before the kernel"). Within these broad categories, cells also may differ from each other in key details of their structure; however, all cells share many of the same components and processes.

One characteristic that appears unique to most (but perhaps not all) living organisms is the ability to maintain **homeostasis**, that is, the ability to maintain constant internal conditions despite a changing external environment. The membrane of a cell helps to maintain homeostasis by regulating what substances can pass into and out of the cell.

The maintenance of homeostasis requires energy, and therefore all living organisms require energy for survival. The ultimate source of energy for nearly all living creatures is the sun. Many organisms have the ability to convert solar energy into chemical energy via a process of **photosynthesis**. This chemical energy helps to maintain homeostasis in photosynthetic organisms and also provides a source of energy for the non-photosynthetic organisms that consume them. Cellular respiration, the process that converts chemical energy stored as a result of photosynthesis into "cellular energy," or ATP, is covered in more detail in Topic 3 of this lab manual.

(20 Minutes)

Instructors: There is no universally agreed-upon set of criteria that mark the existence of life. This discussion exercise is meant to engage students in what we hope is an intriguing exploration of the question "What is life?"

L A B   E X E R C I S E   2 . 1

Defining Life

A. Review the following list. Categorize each item into "living," "not living," or "unsure."

TABLE 2.1

	Living	Not Living	Unsure
Killer whale			
Hair			
Pine tree			
Cow's milk			
Bread mold			
Lava			
Volcano			
Water			
Acorn			
A heart			
HIV (the virus that causes AIDS)			
Elvis Presley			

B. Compare your categorization with other students in the class. On which items was there consensus?

C. Brainstorm a list of attributes that fit all of the consensus "living" items and list them below. Do any of the "non-living" items possess some or all of these attributes?

D. Look at the items that were difficult to classify or about which there was disagreement. Choose one of those items and describe why you believe your categorization is correct. Be prepared to share this answer with the rest of the class.

LAB EXERCISE 2.2

Prokaryotic and Eukaryotic Cells

(45 Minutes)

Materials:
- *Compound microscopes, 1 per student group*
- *Prepared slide of newspaper fragment, 1 per student group*

A. Introduction to the Light Microscope

The unaided eye cannot see structures as small as prokaryotic and eukaryotic cells. In order to visualize these cells, we must use one of the most important tools of biological scientists: the **compound microscope**. Figure 2.1 illustrates a "typical" compound microscope; the scopes in your lab may look different, but should have all of the same basic components.

Compound microscopes are so named because they consist of two sets of glass lenses: the **ocular lens** or lenses, which are near the eye; and the **objective lenses**, which are near the subject of interest.

1. Locate the ocular and objective lenses on the microscope.

   The power of these lenses (that is, their magnification) is typically printed on the side or top of the lens tube. For instance, a 10X lens magnifies objects by 10 times.

   What is the power of the ocular lens on the microscope? _____

   Most compound microscopes contain more than one objective lens. You can move these lenses into position by twisting the **nosepiece** they are attached to.

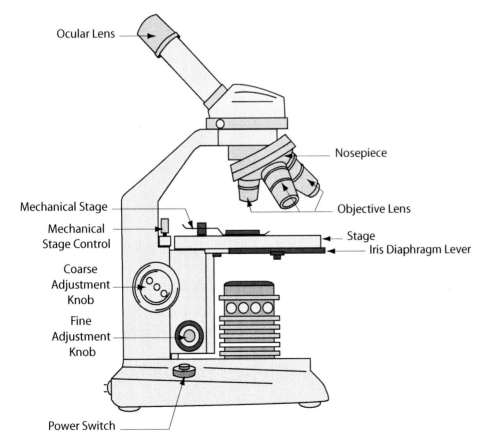

Ocular Lens

Nosepiece

Mechanical Stage

Mechanical Stage Control

Objective Lens

Stage

Iris Diaphragm Lever

Coarse Adjustment Knob

Fine Adjustment Knob

Power Switch

FIGURE 2.1

2. What is the power of each of the objective lenses on the microscope?

_____

The objective lens that is transmitting light to the ocular lenses is the one that is pointing directly at the **stage**, the flat surface immediately below the lens.

3. You can calculate the total magnification power of the microscope at any given objective lens setting by multiplying the magnification of the ocular lens by the magnification of the objective lens. Fill in Table 2.2 with the total magnification obtained using each objective lens.

TABLE 2.2

A. Magnification of ocular lens	B. Magnification of objective	Total magnification (A x B)

4. Notice that the stage contains a hole through which light from below is transmitted.

Locate the on-off switch for the microscope light source. Does the microscope have a brightness control on this switch as well?

_____

A **microscope slide** containing a specimen of interest can be secured on the stage by the clip-like **mechanical stage**. Once the slide is secure, the mechanical stage can be moved left, right, away from you, and toward you by turning the **mechanical stage control** mounted below the stage.

5. Twist the nosepiece containing the objective lenses so that the lowest power objective is facing the stage. Use the **coarse adjustment knob** on the arm of the scope to lower the stage to its lowest point. Making sure that the text on the paper is right side up, secure a slide containing a newspaper fragment to the mechanical stage. Use the mechanical stage control to center the slide so that light is passing through a portion of the newspaper.

6. Look through the ocular lenses. You should see a single bright circle of light. If you see a double circle or can only see through a single ocular lens at a time, the distance between these lenses needs to be adjusted. In most microscopes, adjustment simply requires grasping the tubes of the ocular and pushing them together or pulling them apart. Fiddle with the adjustment until you are comfortably seeing a single circle through the eyepiece. Using the coarse adjustment knob, bring the stage of the microscope up toward the objective lens until the newsprint comes into reasonable focus. The **fine adjustment knob** can be used to further clarify the image. What is the orientation of the text; that is, does it look the same when viewing it without the microscope?_____

7. Reach around to the front of the stage to locate the **iris diaphragm lever** beneath it. This controls the diameter of the hole transmitting light to the specimen on the stage. What happens when you move this lever to the left? _____
What about when you move it to the right? _____

8. Use the mechanical stage control to move the slide to the right as you observe through the ocular. Which way does the slide appear to move?_____

Use the mechanical stage control to move the slide away from you as you observe through the ocular. Which way does the slide appear to move?_____

9. Make sure the image is as sharp as possible. Keeping the stage in place, twist the objective lens nosepiece so that the next higher power objective is in place. If the higher magnified image is out of focus, use the fine adjustment knob only to improve its clarity. **Using the coarse adjustment knob at higher magnifications runs the risk of accidentally grinding the lens into the slide, which can damage both.** Switch to the high power lens and refocus, using only the fine adjustment knob. How does changing the magnification change the brightness of the image?_____

Instructors: The protocol in this exercise requires the use of filamentous bacteria. Oscillatoria is a widely available filamentous cyanobacteria, and prepared slides of this organism can be obtained from biological suppliers. Unfortunately, Oscillatoria cells are about 10X larger than a "typical" bacterial cell. You can either locate a slide of a more typically sized bacterial species (for example, **Bacillus cereus***, or a wet mount of yogurt to see the* **Streptococcus lactis** *and* **Lactobacillus** *species) or make it clear to students that the* Oscillatoria *cells are above average in size.*

Materials:
- *Light microscopes with 100X objectives*
- *Immersion oil*
- *Millimeter scales*
- *Calculators*
- *Prepared slides of* **Oscillatoria** *or another filamentous bacteria*

B. Examining and Measuring Prokaryotic Cells

Compared to eukaryotic cells, prokaryotic cells are very "stripped down" in terms of their internal structure. As a result, they can be much smaller than eukaryotic cells. In this exercise, you will use the microscope to determine the size of a relatively large bacterial cell.

1. Obtain a millimeter scale and place it on the microscope stage. Examine the scale with the scanning (3.5X or 4X) objective lens in place.

2. Estimate the diameter of the field of view by counting the number of 0.1-millimeter "blocks" that span the field of view. Record this diameter to the nearest 0.1 mm.

Diameter of the scanning objective field _____

3. The diameter of the field of view using the scanning objective can be used to calculate the diameter using any other objective by the following formula:

$$\frac{\text{Magnification of scanning objective}}{\text{Magnification of "other" objective}} \times \text{diameter of scanning objective} =$$

Diameter of "other" objective _____

4. Calculate the diameter of the field of view of the highest power objective.

Diameter of the high power field _____

5. Obtain a prepared slide of filamentous bacteria, such as *Oscillatoria*, and view it under the high power objective. Estimate the length and width of a single cell in the filament in millimeters using the following scheme:

Length of a strand that spans the field of view = diameter of field of view

$$\text{Length of a single cell} = \frac{\text{length of the strand}}{\text{number of cells in strand spanning field of view}}$$

Length _____

6. The diameter of a period on this page is approximately 0.1 mm. How many *Oscillatoria* cells would be able to span a period? _____

7. Consider that the *Oscillatoria* you examined is about 10 times larger than a "typical" bacterial cell. How many "typical cells" would be able to span a period that is 0.1mm in diameter? _____

Materials:
- *Culture or prepared slide of* **Paramecium***, enough for all students*
- *Glass slides and coverslips*
- *Dropper bottles of water*
- *Kimwipes*
- *Forceps*
- *Elodea*
- *Methylene blue solution*

C. Examining a Variety of Eukaryotic Cells

1. A Simple Eukaryotic Organism

Obtain a slide or a sample of *Paramecium* and observe these single-celled organisms under high power on the microscope.

Draw one below and label the nucleus and cell membrane.

How is this cell similar to a bacterial cell? How is it different?

2. Animal Cells

   Make a slide of your own skin cells by following the protocol below:

   - Wash your hands and wrists with soap and water. Dry with a clean paper towel.
   - Stick a clean piece of clear tape to the underside of one of your wrists. Press down on the tape so that loose cells will be pulled off when the tape is removed.
   - Carefully remove the piece of tape. Avoid touching the sticky side with your fingers.
   - Place the tape, sticky side up, on a slide. Stain with 2 or 3 drops of methylene blue solution. (Note: Methylene blue will stain clothing, skin, and furniture. Please handle with care.)
   - Place a cover slip over the tape and tap it down slightly.

   Instructors: You may use this protocol for looking at human cells or the more typical cheek cell protocol (students scrape the inside of their cheek with a toothpick and smear it on the slide). The advantage of this protocol is that it is a little neater.

   Observe the cells under the microscope at high power magnification.

   Draw a few cells below, labeling the cell membrane and nucleus.

   How are your skin (epidermal) cells like the *Paramecium*? How are they different?

3. Plant Cells

Take a leaf from the *Elodea* plant available. A smaller leaf near the tip of a shoot is preferable, but any leaf will work. Place the leaf in a droplet of water on a clean microscope slide and cover with a cover slip. Observe the *Elodea* under the highest power magnification on the microscope. Draw what you see below, and label the nucleus, cell wall, and chloroplasts (the green organelles).

How are the *Elodea* cells like your skin cells? How are they different?

Using your calculations from Exercise 2.2B, determine the length of one *Elodea* cell. How does this compare to an *Oscillatoria* cell? How does it compare to a more "typical" bacterium?

LAB EXERCISE 2.3

Homeostasis and the Cell Membrane

(1.5 hours, although there is "down time" to do other exercises between measurements)

Instructors: Be forewarned! This exercise requires a significant amount of pre-class preparation. In our experience, however, students enjoy it and do gain important insights into basic functions of the cell membrane.

Materials:

Per student group:
- *Six chicken eggs, shells removed, in bowl or large beaker. Eggs should be completely immersed in 20% sucrose solution.*
- *Five 250-mL beakers*
- *Large spoon (for moving eggs)*
- *Electronic scale*
- *Marker to label beakers*
- *Supply of paper towels*
- *100 mL of each of the following solutions: distilled water, 10% sucrose, 20% sucrose, 40% sucrose and one of "unknown" concentration (10, 20, or 40%)*

To remove shells from eggs: 3 days before the lab, place eggs in vinegar. The shell should be completely dissolved by the end of the three day period – if any remains, gently rub the surface to remove.

Recipe for sucrose solution: 10% = 100 g table sugar/1 L water, 20% = 200 g table sugar/1 L water, 40% = 400 g table sugar/1 L water.

The membrane of a cell is essential for maintaining a relatively constant environment within the cell. Membranes are thus **selectively permeable**, meaning that the passage of certain materials, but not all materials, is allowed across the membrane. Selective permeability of the cell membrane allows the cell to regulate the composition of its internal environment.

Selective permeability has its limits, however. Some substances, such as water, can freely cross the membrane, whereas other substances—including larger molecules—are blocked from passage or allowed through in a very regulated manner. Because water can move, but solutes cannot, the survival of a cell often depends on the water content of the liquid that it is bathed in. The movement of water across a membrane is called **osmosis**. The following demonstration illustrates the selective permeability of the cell membrane by measuring the effects of osmosis on a large cell.

The yolk of an unfertilized chicken egg is a single, very large cell. The membrane that encloses the yolk and its nutritious albumin accessory fluid (the "egg white") is a selectively permeable cell membrane. The large size of this single cell makes it an ideal model for studying osmosis.

A. Make a prediction about the effects of osmosis.

Eggs that have had their shells dissolved away (in a vinegar bath) have been placed in a solution containing 20% sucrose. The eggs are **isotonic** to this solution, meaning that the concentration of water inside the egg is identical to the concentration of water in the sucrose solution. The cell membrane is impermeable to sucrose. As a result, even though water can freely cross the cell membrane, there is no net flow of water in either direction — that is, the same number of water molecules leaves the egg as enters it from the surrounding solution. If the solution is **hypotonic** to the eggs, meaning that the concentration of solutes is lower in the solution than in the eggs, the net flow of water across the cell membrane should be into the egg. If the solution is **hypertonic**, meaning that there is a higher concentration of solutes in the solution than in the egg, the net flow of water across the membrane should be out of the egg.

You will now predict whether the egg will gain or lose water in solutions of different tonicity. Be prepared to share your predictions, and your justifications for those predictions, with your instructor and classmates.

TABLE 2.3

Solution	Tonicity (Isotonic, hypertonic, or hypotonic)	Result (Egg will gain water, lose water, or remain the same)
0% sucrose		
10% sucrose		
20% sucrose		
40% sucrose		

B. Test your hypotheses.

1. Obtain 5 beakers from your laboratory instructor. Fill one with 0% sucrose solution (that is, plain distilled water), one with 10% sucrose solution, one with 20% sucrose solution, one with 40% sucrose solution, and one with a "mystery" solution provided by your instructor. Be sure to label the beakers with the percent sucrose solution they contain.

2. Obtain 5 chicken eggs in 20% sucrose from your laboratory instructor. Handling the eggs carefully so as not to break the membrane, remove them one by one from the solution, dry them gently with a paper towel and weigh them (separately) on the electronic balance. For each egg, record its weight on Table 2.3 and then place it immediately in the corresponding beaker.

3. Weigh the eggs again at 15-minute intervals for 1 hour. Be sure to dry the eggs (gently) before recording their weights. Record these weights in Table 2.4.

TABLE 2.4

Weight of eggs in solution ⟶	0% sucrose	10% sucrose	20% sucrose	40% sucrose	unknown
Time ↓					
0 minutes					
15 minutes					
30 minutes					
45 minutes					
60 minutes					

4. Calculate the change in weight for each time interval using the following equation, and record your data in Table 2.5.

Weight at current time interval − initial weight of egg = weight change

TABLE 2.5

Weight change of eggs in solution ⟶	0% sucrose	10% sucrose	20% sucrose	40% sucrose	unknown
Time ↓					
0 minutes					
15 minutes					
30 minutes					
45 minutes					
60 minutes					

5. Review the following questions and be prepared to share your answers with your instructor and your classmates:

a. Which solutions caused the eggs to gain weight? Which caused them to lose it?

Eggs in 0% and 10% sucrose solution should gain weight; eggs in 40% solution should lose weight. (What happens in the unknown solution depends on the sucrose concentration...)

b. Why did the eggs gain or lose weight?

Water crossed the egg membrane, but sucrose could not. Thus, eggs in the hypotonic solution gained weight and the eggs in the hypertonic solution lost weight. Any eggs in an isotonic solution stayed the same.

c. What was the concentration of sucrose in the "unknown" solution? How do you know?

Weight change of the egg in the unknown solution should be similar to the weight change of an egg in the equivalent solution.

d. If an egg was placed in 30% sucrose solution, would it gain or lose weight? Explain your reasoning.

It should lose weight, since the solution is hypertonic to the egg.

e. How would the results of this experiment be different if both water and sucrose could cross the egg cell membrane? How would it be different if neither water nor sucrose could cross the egg cell membrane?

In both cases, the weight of the egg should not change. (However, if the rate of sucrose passage was slower than the rate of water passage, eggs that were permeable to both sucrose and water might increase in weight in the hypotonic solution initially [and then decrease as the sucrose slowly equalized] and decrease in weight in the hypertonic solution.)

f. If egg cells were permeable to sucrose, how could the egg maintain homeostasis of sucrose concentration despite a changing external environment? How does the cell membrane make homeostasis for sucrose concentration easier to maintain?

The egg might not be able to maintain homeostasis of sucrose concentration without some significant expenditure of energy. For instance, it could move to remain in a constant sucrose environment, or it could have a process for converting sucrose to starch or another polysaccharide and back again in order to keep sucrose levels regulated. The selective permeability of the cell membrane offers a much less energy-intensive mechanism for maintaining internal conditions.

LAB EXERCISE 2.4

The Requirements for Photosynthesis

Most organisms on Earth depend on photosynthesis either directly or indirectly to provide the energy needed for survival. Photosynthesis is a complex process, but one with a few relatively simple requirements to proceed. This simple protocol elegantly demonstrates the process of photosynthesis and helps identify its raw materials. In it, we will use phenol red, a chemical indicator for carbon dioxide (CO_2). Phenol red turns yellow in the presence of CO_2 and is pink in its absence.

A. Determine what raw materials are required for photosynthesis.

1. Find the four clean test tubes at your lab bench. If the tubes are not clean, rinse them thoroughly with tap water. Label the tubes 1 through 4.
2. Fill each tube 1/2 full with tap water. Add 10 drops of phenol red to each tube and mix, using a drinking straw as a stirrer. The water should be noticeably pink—if it is not, add more phenol red.
3. Using the straw, carefully blow into tubes 1, 2, and 3 until the phenol red solution *just* turns yellow. (When you blow into the solution, you are dissolving CO_2 from your lungs in the water and the indicator turns from pink to yellow.)
4. Cut two 3-inch long pieces of *Elodea*, an aquatic flowering plant, from the center table. Place a piece in each of tubes 1 and 2. The *Elodea* should be completely covered by the water. Place a cork in the top of each tube.
5. Cover tube 2 with a piece of aluminum foil. Be sure the foil completely blocks out all light.

(1 hour total; 15 minutes to set up, 40 minutes to "run," 10 minutes to collect data.)

Materials:
- *Large test tubes (4 per lab group)*
- *Test tube racks*
- *Corks for test tubes*
- *Soda straws (Note: a reviewer suggested the use of coffee stirrers in place of straws, to better control the rate of carbon dioxide addition to the solution)*
- *Dilute phenol red in dropper bottles*
- *Lamps*
- *Aluminum foil*
- **Elodea** *shoots*

6. If you can, place the tubes in the tube holder in direct sunlight. If there is no direct sunlight, place a bright, incandescent light near the sides of the tubes.

7. After 45 minutes, observe and record any color changes in Table 2.6.

TABLE 2.6

	Color at Beginning	**Plant**	**Light Conditions**	**Results**
Tube 1	yellow	*Elodea*	light	
Tube 2	yellow	*Elodea*	dark	
Tube 3	yellow	no plant	light	
Tube 4	pink	no plant	light	

8. Discuss the following questions with your lab partners. Be prepared to share your answers with your lab instructor and the class:

a. In which tube(s) has photosynthesis occurred? How can you tell?

Photosynthesis occurred in tube 1 only because the indicator has turned pink, which tells us that the carbon dioxide we had dissolved in the water is gone.

b. What is the purpose of tube 3 in the experiment?

To see if carbon dioxide would naturally be lost from the system when it is exposed to light, even in the absence of photosynthesis. If the indicator had turned pink in this tube despite the lack of a plant, we could not conclude that photosynthesis had occurred in tube one with a plant present.

c. What is the purpose of tube 4 in the experiment?

To determine whether the indicator changes color over the course of 45 minutes and to provide a basis for comparing the degree of color change in the various tubes.

TOPIC 2
_____

POST-LABORATORY QUIZ

CELLS AND ENERGY

1. Define one characteristic shared by all living organisms.
   Several answers possible. A common one will be homeostasis, the ability to maintain internal conditions in the face of changing external environments.

2. List two differences between prokaryotes and eukaryotes.
   Prokaryotes: no nucleus, very small size. Eukaryotes: contain nucleus, larger size (other organelle differences [e.g. chloroplast, mitochondria] acceptable as possible answers).

3. You are examining a microscope slide of cells from the skin of an onion under low power. In order to see more details within the nucleus of the cell, you switch to high power. How do you refine the clearness of this image?
   Use ONLY the fine adjustment knob to improve the focus.

4. You are examining some onion skin under the microscope and wish to determine the length of the cells you are observing. If the diameter of the field of view is 0.250 millimeters, and 2.5 cells fit across that diameter, what is the length of the cells?
   0.100 millimeters (100 micrometers)

5. List two differences between plant and animal cells.
   Plant cells have a cell wall and chloroplasts, animal cells do not. (Other differences listed may be acceptable as well — vacuole, photosynthesis, centrioles.)

6. The movement of water across a cell membrane is called _____. Water crosses the cell membrane, but other substances do not, because the membrane is _____.
   Osmosis, selectively permeable

7. If a de-shelled chicken egg containing 20% solutes is placed in a 30% sucrose solution, what will happen to the weight of the egg, and why?

   The egg will lose weight, as the net flow of water is out of the egg and into the solution.

8. What do photosynthetic cells require in order to transform light energy into chemical energy?

   Light, carbon dioxide

9. An *Elodea* plant is placed in water containing the indicator phenol red. Carbon dioxide is then added to the water and the plant is placed in a dark room. After one hour, what color do you expect the indicator solution to be, and why?

   Yellow, since adding carbon dioxide will turn it this color, and the carbon dioxide will not be consumed by photosynthesis unless the plant is exposed to light.

10. What is the ultimate source of energy for life for <u>nearly all</u> living organisms on Earth?

    The sun

TOPIC 3

Nutrition and Metabolism

A pre-laboratory quiz is available in Appendix A on page 201.

Learning Objectives

1. Describe the structure and function of enzymes.
2. Demonstrate that processing foods can denature enzymes.
3. Understand the role of mitochondria in producing cellular energy.
4. Demonstrate that carbon dioxide is produced during cellular respiration.
5. Understand how heart rate can be used as a measure of fitness.
6. Determine basal metabolic rate and analyze a diet.

Pre-laboratory Reading

The food you eat goes through a series of conversions before it can be used to produce energy. When you swallow food, it moves from your mouth to your esophagus. The esophagus brings food to the stomach, where the further breakdown of food into its subunits occurs. Food then travels through the small intestine for further digestion and then to the large intestine. Substances that cannot be broken down exit the body after passing through the large intestine.

While in the stomach and small intestine, proteins called **enzymes** break the food down and release it into the bloodstream, where it is transported to individual cells. Enzymes function to speed up, or **catalyze**, the rate of metabolic reactions. Each enzyme catalyzes a particular reaction, a property called **specificity**. The specificity of an enzyme is the result of its shape. Different enzymes have different shapes because each one is composed of a unique series of amino acids. The 20 amino acids each have different side groups, and are arranged in unique orders for each enzyme. This diversity in amino acid arrangement produces enzymes of various shapes and sizes. Enzymes can be broken down, or **denatured**, by heat or chemical treatments. After an enzyme has been denatured, it can no longer perform its cellular job.

Substances that are acted upon by enzymes are called the enzyme's **substrate**. The specificity of an enzyme for its substrate occurs because the enzyme can only bind to a substrate whose shape conforms to the enzyme's shape. The region on the enzyme where the substrate binds is called the enzyme's **active site**. The enzyme binds its substrate, helps convert it to a reaction product, and then resumes its original shape so it can perform the reaction again. A denatured enzyme loses its native shape and may no longer be able to bind its substrate.

After being broken down by the digestive system and delivered to individual cells, the products of digestion are used by organelles called **mitochondria**, located inside your body's cells (see Figure 3.1).

Mitochondria are kidney-bean-shaped organelles surrounded by two membranes, the inner and outer mitochondrial membranes. The inner membrane houses some of the proteins involved in producing ATP (adenosine triphosphate). The space between the two membranes is called the **intermembrane space**. Inside the inner membrane is the semifluid matrix of the mitochondrion, where some of the enzymes involved in producing ATP are located. Once inside mitochondria, the nutrients in food undergo a process called **cellular respiration**.

During cellular respiration, cells use oxygen and produce carbon dioxide and water (this is why you breathe in oxygen and breathe out carbon dioxide). During this process, the energy stored in the chemical bonds of nutrients is used to produce ATP. The ATP produced can then be used to power cellular

Mitochondrion

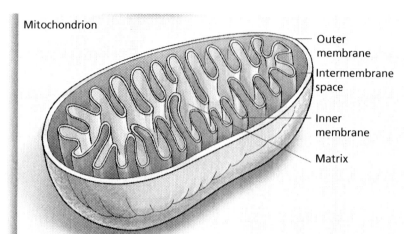

Outer membrane

Intermembrane space

Inner membrane

Matrix

Eukaryotic cells contain mitochondria. Mitochondria are energy-producing organelles surrounded by two membranes. The inner and outer mitochondrial membranes are separated by the intermembrane space. The highly convoluted inner membrane carries many of the proteins involved in producing ATP. The matrix of the mitochondrion is the location of many of the reactions of cellular respiration.

FIGURE 3.1

activities, such as helping an enzyme perform its job. Cellular respiration occurs in the mitochondria of both plant and animal cells. The following equation summarizes the process of cellular respiration of a glucose molecule:

$$C_6H_{12}O_6 + 6O_2 \longrightarrow 6CO_2 + 6H_2O$$

glucose + oxygen yields carbon dioxide + water

Glucose is an energy-rich compound, but the products of its digestion—carbon dioxide and water—are energy poor. The energy released during the conversion of glucose to carbon dioxide and water is used to synthesize ATP.

Cellular respiration occurs at different rates in different individuals. When more Calories are consumed than used, energy is stored as fat. When fewer Calories are consumed than used, weight loss occurs. Your heart rate, in part, determines the rate of cellular respiration because the heart pumps oxygen to cells so that respiration can occur. The more efficient your heart is, the less work it has to do to supply your cells with oxygen.

(45 Minutes)

LAB EXERCISE 3.1

Enzymatic Breakdown of Collagen

Materials (per lab group):
- *Three 1/2" gelatin cubes*
- *15 mL fresh pineapple juice (1 medium pineapple gives around 100 mL juice)*
- *15 mL pineapple juice prepared from canned pineapple chunks (each 20 oz. can produces around 50 mL of juice)*
- *Knives*
- *Blender*
- *Cheesecloth*

Suggestions:
- *Add 14 g of unflavored gelatin to 400 mL of boiling water, and pour into shallow pan to depth of about 1/2 inch. Cool in refrigerator and slice into 1/2-inch cubes.*
- *To shorten the length of time students spend on this exercise, you can prepare the juice from both fresh and canned pineapple before class.*
- *Rinse knives, blender, and so on between treatments.*

Canning is a type of food processing that involves heating foods to high temperatures to kill any bacteria that might be present. In addition to killing microbes, proteins present in canned food can be denatured.

Collagen is a fibrous protein that serves as a structural subunit of bone, cartilage, and tendon. Boiling collagen converts the fibrous protein into a more gelatinous form. Collagen also serves as a substrate for the enzyme bromelin. Bromelin, present in plants called bromeliads, metabolizes collagen.

A. Witness the actions of the enzyme bromelin on collagen in gelatin.

1. Devise a hypothesis that predicts how the condition of gelatin may be affected by exposure to fresh and canned pineapple juice. Pineapple is a bromeliad.

2. Fill a beaker to 50 mL with fresh pineapple, cut in 1-inch chunks. After measuring, place the pineapple in a blender and puree for 1–2 minutes. Strain the puree through cheesecloth to remove the pulp.

3. Clean the blender and repeat this procedure using chunks of canned pineapple.

4. Add one 1/2-inch cube of gelatin to each of three test tubes. Press the gelatin to the bottom of the tube. Label the test tubes A, B, and C.

5. Pour 5 mL of freshly prepared pineapple juice into test tube A and 5 mL of juice from the canned pineapple into test tube B. Add 5 mL water to test tube C.

6. What is the purpose of tube C?

   Control to see how untreated gelatin holds up

7. Using numbers from 1-10 (1 for water; 10 for chunky) record your observations every 5 minutes for 30 minutes in Table 3.1. (You can perform Exercises 3.2 and 3.3 while these reactions are running.)

TABLE 3.1

	0 Minutes	5 Minutes	10 Minutes	15 Minutes	20 Minutes	25 Minutes	30 Minutes
Gelatin + fresh pineapple	10						
Gelatin + canned pineapple	10						
Gelatin and water	10						

8. Do your results support your hypothesis? Why or why not?

LAB EXERCISE 3.2

Examining Mitochondria

After food has been digested in the stomach and small intestine, it is transported to cells for further breakdown. Mitochondria are kidney-bean-shaped organelles found inside cells that help continue the breakdown process.

A. Stain plant cells to visualize mitochondria.

1. On a clean glass slide, mix three drops of the stain Janus Green B with one drop of 7% sucrose.

2. Prepare a very thin piece of red onion epidermis by removing a fleshy portion of the bulb and snapping the modified leaf backward. Look carefully at the point at which the onion snapped. Remove the thinnest section of onion that you can recover from the break point. Place the section in the stain you placed on the slide and add a cover slip.

3. Place the slide under the microscope, on low power, and focus on the edge of the section. The stained mitochondria will appear as small blue spheres. Rotate the nosepiece of the microscope to view on higher power.

4. Draw the onion cell and mitochondria you saw under the microscope.

(20 Minutes)

Instructors: In the interest of saving time, you can order prepared slides that have had their mitochondria stained. To save even more time, set this up as a demonstration.

Materials:
- *1 dropper bottle of Janus Green B stain per class*
- *1 glass slide and cover slip per group*
- *1 dropper bottle of 7% sucrose per class*
- *1 fresh red onion per class*
- *1 light microscope per group*

LAB EXERCISE 3.3

Carbon Dioxide Production During Cellular Respiration

The mitochondria that you viewed in the previous exercise use oxygen to convert food energy into the form of energy your cells can use, ATP. Cells undergoing this process release carbon dioxide. When cellular respiration occurs in your body, oxygen enters your cells when you breathe it in through your lungs, and it is transported to your cells by red blood cells. The carbon dioxide that is produced is carried through the blood to the lungs and released.

(30 Minutes)

Materials:
- *0.004% solution of bromothymol blue (150 μL/tube or 450 μL/group)*
- *3 test tubes per group*
- *3 drinking straws per group*
- *Pasteur pipette with rubber bulb*

The release of carbon dioxide can be measured by using an indicator solution called bromothymol blue. As carbon dioxide accumulates, the bromothymol blue turns yellow and is therefore an indicator of carbon dioxide concentration.

A. Measure carbon dioxide production at rest and with exercise.

1. In this exercise, you will measure carbon dioxide production at rest and with exercise. Propose a hypothesis about how carbon dioxide levels might change at rest and with exercise.

2. Place three drops of 0.004% bromothymol blue into each of three test tubes numbered 1–3.

3. One group member should be seated at rest for three minutes. At the end of the rest period, make a note of the time or start your timer. Have the rested group member exhale by gently blowing, at normal breathing intervals, through a drinking straw into the bromothymol blue in test tube 1. Time how long it takes for the solution to change color and record your data in Table 3.2.

TABLE 3.2

Activity level	Time
At rest	
Active	
Atmosphere	

4. The same group member should do as many jumping jacks as possible in three minutes and then blow through the straw into the tube with each exhalation. Time how long it takes for the solution to change color in test tube 2.

5. Use a rubber bulb attached to the end of a Pasteur pipette to blow atmospheric air into the bromothymol blue in test tube 3 until there is a color change. How long did it take for a color change to occur?

6. Compare the results seen in test tubes 1–3. Do the results of this test support your hypothesis? Why or why not?

Increased breathing with exercise should turn indicator yellow faster than breathing without exercise.

7. Why was it important that the same group member performed steps 3 and 4?

To control for differences in breathing rates and carbon dioxide production.

(10 Minutes)

Materials: Calculators

LAB EXERCISE 3.4

Heart Rate as Measure of Healthfulness

Aerobic exercise—exercise that uses oxygen—includes activities such as running, swimming, or biking. Aerobic exercise helps improve the fitness of your heart and its associated blood vessels, thereby improving your cardiovascular fitness. Measuring your heart rate during exercise can help you determine how hard your heart has to work to supply oxygen to your tissues for cellular respiration.

Knowing how to monitor your heart rate allows you to determine whether you are working out too intensely, which is dangerous for your heart, or not hard enough, which is less productive. For a given individual, a range of heart rates provides the most cardiovascular benefit. To maximize the benefits of your aerobic workout, you need to stay within this range of heart rates for at least 20 to 30 minutes.

A. Determine your heart rate.

To determine your range of target heart rates, you must first measure your **resting heart rate**. Your resting heart rate is the rate at which your heart is pumping when you have been sleeping or sitting quietly for a while.

1. To estimate your resting heart rate, count the number of pulses at the carotid artery by pressing gently on one side of your neck, under your chin. You can count for 60 seconds to obtain the number of beats per minute (bpm) or for 6 seconds and multiply that number by 10. If you have been moving around during lab, subtract 15 bpm from the number you counted to estimate your actual resting heart rate. What is your estimated resting heart rate? _____

The typical adult has a resting heart rate of 60–80 bpm, whereas highly trained athletes may have readings of 40 bpm or lower. As you become fit, your resting heart rate should decrease.

Your **maximum heart rate** is the highest number of beats per minute your heart should reach while exercising. This can be estimated by subtracting your age from 220.

2. What is your estimated maximum heart rate? _____
3. To calculate your target zone, first multiply your maximum heart rate by 60% (.6), then by 80% (.8). What is your target zone? _____

As an athlete increases his cardiovascular fitness, he will be able to train for longer periods of time and more intensely without increasing his heart rate above the maximum for his target zone. This means that the athlete's heart is becoming stronger and more efficient.

LAB EXERCISE 3.5

Food and Energy

(20 Minutes)

Materials: Calculator
Suggestions: If you want students to analyze their own diets, you might want to warn them a week in advance of this lab or have them turn in their analyses the following week.

Just as different individuals have different target heart rates, different individuals also have different energy use efficiencies. The **metabolic rate** of an individual is a measure of his or her energy use. The metabolic rate changes according to an individual's activity level. The **basal metabolic rate (BMR)** is a measure of the energy used by an awake, alert person. This rate differs among individuals based on height, weight, age, and gender. You can estimate your BMR and use that information to calculate your daily caloric needs using a formula called the Harris Benedict formula.

Using the Harris Benedict formula to determine caloric needs is more accurate than measurements based solely on body weight. This is because two individuals who weigh the same amount might differ in exercise levels, age, height, and gender. An important factor that this formula does not take into account is body fat percentage, because this is often not known and is difficult to determine. Keep in mind that leaner, more muscular bodies need more Calories because muscle is more energy costly than fat. Therefore, this equation is especially accurate for people who are not very muscular or very fat.

A. Determine the number of Calories required to maintain your weight.

1. Determine your BMR.

BMR for women = 665 + (9.6 × weight in kilos)

+ (1.7 × height in cm) − (4.7 × age in years)

BMR for men = 66 + (13.7 × weight in kilos)

+ (5 × height in cm) − (6.8 × age in years)

Notes:

1 inch = 2.54 cm

1 kilogram = 2.2 lbs

For example, Jean weighs 130 pounds and is 5′ 4″ tall.

Her weight in kilograms is 130 lbs × 1kg/2.2lbs = 59 kg.

Her height in cm is 64 inches × 2.54 cm/inch = 162.56 cm.

Your BMR = _____

2. Multiply your BMR by a factor that describes your activity level.

Sedentary activity (little or no exercise) = BMR × 1.2
Light activity (exercise 1 − 3 days/week) = BMR × 1.375
Moderate activity (exercise 3 − 5 days/week) = BMR × 1.55
Heavy activity (hard exercise 5 − 7 days/week) = BMR × 1.725

BMR × activity factor = _____

This is the total number of Calories you need to maintain your current weight.

B. Determine whether a particular diet is balanced.

In a healthy diet, the percentage of Calories obtained from protein should be around 0.8 grams per 2.2 lbs of body weight. The percentage of Calories from fat should be at least 10% but not more than 30%. The remaining Calories should be provided by carbohydrates.

1. Helen is a 150-pound, 20-year-old college junior. A typical day's food for Helen consists of around 2,000 Calories, composed of 60 grams of protein, 70 grams of fat, and 282.5 grams of carbohydrate. Calculate the percentage of Calories provided by each nutrient (protein and carbohydrate are 4 Calories/gram, fat is 9 Calories/gram) and determine whether Helen is getting the right percentages of each nutrient.

60 g protein × 4 C/g = 240 C
70 g fat × 9 C/g = 630 C
282.5 g carb × 4 C/g = 1130 C

% protein = 240/2000 = 12%
% fat = 630/2000 = 31.5%
% carb = 1130/2000 = 56.5%

Helen is eating a little too much fat.

2. The only other things Helen should be concerned about are getting enough vitamins, minerals, fibers, and water. What types of foods would be most beneficial in this regard?
Fruits, veggies, meat, and dairy

3. Track your own diet for a few days and calculate the percentage of your diet that is fat, carbohydrate, and protein.

TOPIC 3
_____

POST-LABORATORY QUIZ

NUTRITION AND METABOLISM

1. Describe how enzymes catalyze metabolic reactions.
   Substrate fits into active site and is converted to product.

2. Different enzymes are composed of different sequences of ___*amino acids*___ .

3. What does the enzyme bromelin do, and why did this not occur when the canned pineapple was used?
   The bromelin in the canned pineapple had been heated. The enzyme might have been denatured and was no longer effective.

4. List the reactants and products of cellular respiration.
   Reactants are glucose and oxygen. Products are carbon dioxide and water.

5. The products of digestion are used to produce ATP in organelles called ___*mitochondria*___ .

6. The ___*basal metabolic rate*___ represents the resting energy use of an awake, alert person.

7. List several factors that affect a person's BMR:
   Gender, age, efficiency of enzymes.

8. Do proteins, carbohydrates, or fats have the most Calories per gram?
   Fats.

9. Why is a fit person's heart rate slower than that of an unfit person?
   Heart more efficiently delivers oxygen to tissues.

10. If a very muscular person used the Harris Benedict formula to calculate daily Calorie needs, would the number of Calories they calculated actually be an overestimate or an underestimate? Why? What if an overweight person used the Harris Benedict formula? Would they overestimate or underestimate their daily Caloric needs?
    Muscular people will underestimate caloric needs because lean muscle mass uses more energy than fat. Overweight people will overestimate their caloric needs because it takes less energy to supply fat than muscle.

TOPIC 4

Mitosis

Learning Objectives

1. Describe the cell cycle.
2. Illustrate the chromosomal condition and significance of each stage of mitosis.
3. Examine the rate of cell division in various tissues.
4. List several ways in which normal cell division is regulated.
5. Explain how mutations to cell cycle control genes can result in tumors.
6. Describe how scientists determine the cancer risk associated with various chemicals and activities.

A pre-laboratory quiz is available in Appendix A on page 203.

Pre-laboratory Reading

The process by which cells increase in number by making copies of themselves is called **cell division**. In all **eukaryotic cells** (cells containing a nucleus and membrane-bound organelles), the stages of cell division are nearly identical and are collectively known as **mitosis**. Mitosis is one part of the **cell cycle**—a process that includes stages known as **interphase** and **cytokinesis**. The relationship among these phases is diagrammed in Figure 4.1.

As you can see in Figure 4.1, the genetic material inside the cell is duplicated during interphase. Mitosis results in the equal division of this DNA into two daughter cells, and cytokinesis cleaves the single cell into two.

DNA in eukaryotic cells is found in linear structures known as **chromosomes**. A typical human chromosome carries hundreds of genes along its length and is found in a thin, tangled, thread-like form during interphase. Most human cells carry two copies of each chromosome—these pairs are not identical, but they are equivalent, with each member of the pair carrying the same genes.

(a)

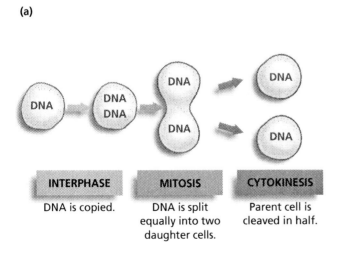

INTERPHASE	MITOSIS	CYTOKINESIS
DNA is copied.	DNA is split equally into two daughter cells.	Parent cell is cleaved in half.

(b)

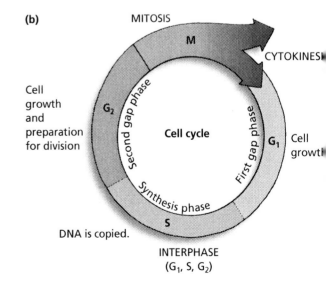

FIGURE 4.1

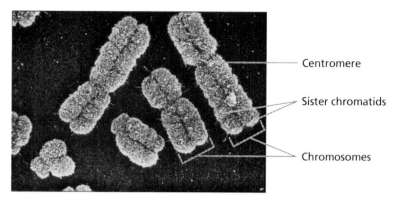

Centromere

Sister chromatids

Chromosomes

FIGURE 4.2

During the first stage of mitosis, known as **prophase**, chromosomes condense into tightly wound, compact forms that are easily visualized under a light microscope. At the end of prophase, the membrane surrounding the nucleus has disappeared and we can easily see individual, already duplicated chromosomes. Each chromosome consists of two identical strands called **sister chromatids**, which are attached to each other at a structure called the **centromere** (Figure 4.2).

The second and third stages of mitosis, **metaphase** and **anaphase**, allow for the systematic separation of sister chromatids into two identical daughter cells, each containing a full set of chromosomes. During metaphase, the duplicated chromosomes are aligned across the middle of each cell—the chromosomes are moved to this position by the actions of **microtubules**, protein structures that radiate out from **centrioles** at the two poles of the cell and attach to the centromere of each chromosome. Aligning the chromosomes at the middle of the cell ensures that each daughter cell will contain one copy of each chromosome. The sister chromatids of each chromosome are separated during anaphase as the microtubules contract toward the poles of the cell. After the sister chromatids are separated, they are each referred to as chromosomes.

The final stage of mitosis is known as **telophase**, during which the nuclear membrane reforms and the chromosomes decondense and become diffuse and threadlike once more. The details of cytokinesis vary among the kingdoms of eukaryotes, but result in the formation of two separate cells. The process of mitosis is illustrated in Figure 4.3.

The purpose of cell division is to allow some cells to reproduce, replace damaged or dead cells, and help tissues and organs grow. Thus, not all cells in the body go through the cell cycle at the same rate and at the same time. Tissues where rapid cell replacement is necessary, such as skin and the lining of the digestive system, will have many cells in various stages of mitosis at any one time. Tissues where cell damage is more rare, such as the liver or heart muscle, will have fewer cells undergoing mitosis. When cell division is working properly, it is tightly controlled; that is, cells are given signals for when, and when not, to divide. Cells that somehow escape this control become **cancerous**, meaning that they are dividing without control. Cancer cells escape cell cycle control because one or more of the genes that affect the process of cell division have been damaged, or **mutated**.

Genes that encode for proteins that regulate the cell cycle are called **proto-oncogenes**. When they are mutated, they are called **oncogenes**—or "cancer genes." Many proto-oncogenes encode for **growth factors** or encode for proteins that respond to the presence of growth factors. A normal growth factor stimulates division only when the cellular environment is favorable and all of the conditions for division have been met. Other proto-oncogenes are **tumor suppressors**, coding for proteins that suppress cell division if conditions are not favorable. These proteins detect and repair DNA damage. Tumor suppressor proteins prevent uncontrolled division when a growth factor or cell division gene mutates and becomes nonfunctional. For cancer to occur, both types of genes in a single cell must be mutated.

After a cell escapes cell cycle control and tumor suppression, it will continue to divide. If the cell is in a relatively immobile tissue, a mass of cells, called a **tumor**, forms. Additional mutations within tumor cells can enable the cancer to spread to other tissues and increase its rate of growth. The excess cells produced by cancer rob other tissues of energy and interfere with the normal functioning of the body.

Cancer-causing mutations to DNA occur most often as a result of the action of DNA-damaging factors called **carcinogens**. There are many known carcinogens, including ultraviolet light, tobacco smoke, and pesticides such as DDT. There are also many suspected carcinogens—chemicals and other environmental factors that can potentially cause DNA damage, but that do not have a clearly established link to human cancers. Carcinogens and suspected carcinogens are also known as cancer **risk factors**. The branch of biology called **epidemiology** investigates the relationship among risk factors and disease. Cancer epidemiologists attempt to determine whether exposure to a particular risk factor is associated with a higher risk of a particular form of cancer, typically by retroactively surveying individuals with that form of cancer, but also by exposing other animals to the risk factor. Epidemiologists also devise strategies for reducing individual exposure to known or suspected carcinogens.

LAB EXERCISE 4.1

Model the Process of Mitosis

A. This simple exercise is designed to help you visualize the dynamic process of mitosis. Use the illustrations in the pre-laboratory reading to help you walk through this process.

1. Obtain *three pairs* of pipe cleaners. Each pair should be a different color. Both members of the pair should be labeled with the same letters, although these letters do not need to be both uppercase or both lowercase in any pair.

   Each pipe cleaner represents a chromosome, and the labels represent a single gene on the chromosome. This set of chromosomes represents the genetic material found in a cell at the beginning of interphase. Illustrate the entire cell at this stage by placing the pipe cleaners on your lab table, encircling them with twine indicating the nuclear membrane, and encircling the nucleus with yet another strand of twine, indicating the cell membrane. Place two of the centriole spools in the cell, outside the nuclear membrane.

2. You can illustrate the chromosome duplication that occurs during interphase simply by obtaining a duplicate of each of the pipe cleaners in your original collection. The duplicates should be identical to the original; in other words, the letter indicating the gene on the duplicate should be the same case as the original. "Clip" each pair of chromosomes together with the available centromeres. Replace the duplicated chromosomes in the nucleus.

3. Illustrate prophase of mitosis by removing the twine symbolizing the nuclear membrane, which dissolves at this stage. Move the centrioles to the poles of the cell (top and bottom) and unravel the "microtubules" from each. Wrap a strand of microtubule wire from each centriole to

(30 Minutes)

Instructors: This exercise is a basic illustration of the process of mitosis using simple materials. Students might object to the "elementary school craft project" feel of the exercise; focus the students on the learning that they are doing, not the materials. The point of the exercise is to help students become more familiar with some of the specialized terminology of cell division as well as to provide another means of helping students visualize how a cell duplicates itself—a process that is not always easy for students to "get" from static illustrations and even animations. You should move about the room during this exercise, checking for understanding and helping students through rough spots.

One way to make this exercise even more interactive is to wait for all groups to finish modeling the process once, and then randomly call on groups to present one stage of mitosis. You can gather the rest of the class around their lab bench as a group describes what is going on in the cell during the stage they are describing.
Materials:

- *Pipe cleaners, 3 different colors, cut to 10-cm lengths. At least 4 of each color per student group. Each color pipe cleaner represents one chromosome. Each should have one "gene" labeled—a tag of masking or labeling tape with a letter inked on it. Half of the pipe cleaners of each color should be labeled with the uppercase letter, half with the lowercase letter. If you plan on doing the laboratory on Inheritance of Traits (Topic 5), use some of the gene labels from that lab so that you can*

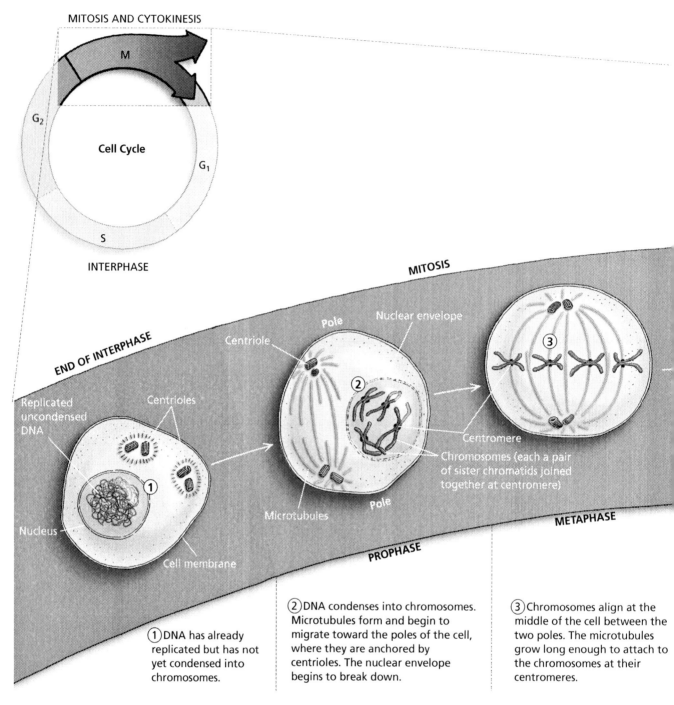

MITOSIS AND CYTOKINESIS

Cell Cycle

G_2

G_1

S

INTERPHASE

END OF INTERPHASE

MITOSIS

Pole

Centriole

Nuclear envelope

③

Replicated
uncondensed
DNA

Centrioles

②

Centromere

Chromosomes (each a pair
of sister chromatids joined
together at centromere)

①

Nucleus

Microtubules

Pole

METAPHASE

Cell membrane

PROPHASE

①DNA has already
replicated but has not
yet condensed into
chromosomes.

②DNA condenses into chromosomes.
Microtubules form and begin to
migrate toward the poles of the cell,
where they are anchored by
centrioles. The nuclear envelope
begins to break down.

③Chromosomes align at the
middle of the cell between the
two poles. The microtubules
grow long enough to attach to
the chromosomes at their
centromeres.

FIGURE 4.3

*reuse these pipe cleaners. (You can ask stu-
dents to consider how a pipe cleaner is a rea-
sonably good model for a chromosome—it's
flexible and "fuzzy"—and how it is a poor
model—not double stranded, no histones
(although histones are not discussed in
Biology: Science for Life).*

- *"Centromeres"—clear pony beads, available at any craft store.*
- *Twine, two different colors—one color to
symbolize nuclear membrane, another to
symbolize cell membrane.*

different sister chromatids in each duplicated chromosome. The wire
should be as close to the centromere as possible, and both chromatids
should be attached to the microtubules at the same side of the centromere (see Figure 4.4 on page 40).

4. Illustrate metaphase of mitosis by pulling the centrioles toward opposite poles so that their attached chromosomes are lined up at the equator of the cell.

5. Illustrate anaphase of mitosis by sliding the centromere off each pair of
sister chromatids and by winding up the microtubules on each centriole.

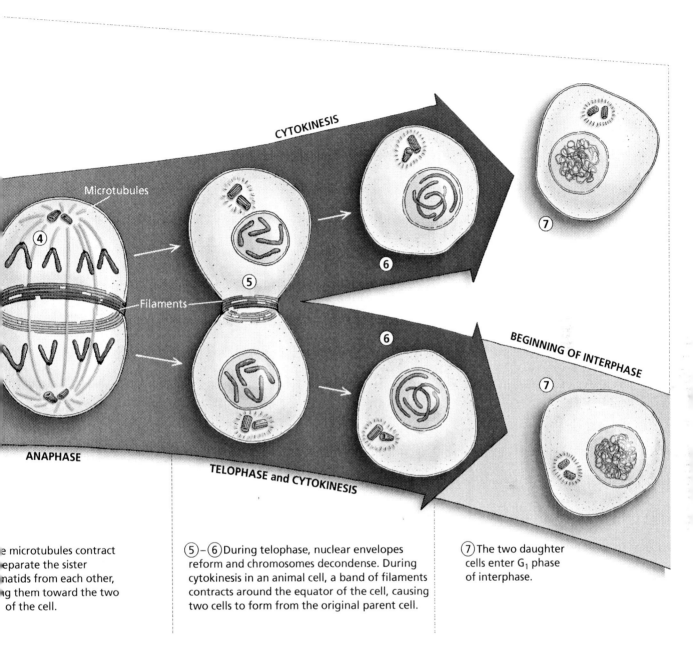

Microtubules

④

Filaments

⑤

⑥

⑥

CYTOKINESIS

⑦

BEGINNING OF INTERPHASE

⑦

⑦

ANAPHASE

TELOPHASE and CYTOKINESIS

e microtubules contract
eparate the sister
natids from each other,
ig them toward the two
of the cell.

⑤–⑥ During telophase, nuclear envelopes
reform and chromosomes decondense. During
cytokinesis in an animal cell, a band of filaments
contracts around the equator of the cell, causing
two cells to form from the original parent cell.

⑦ The two daughter
cells enter G$_1$ phase
of interphase.

This should cause each chromatid to move away from its sister, toward
opposite poles of the cell.

6. Illustrate telophase of mitosis by pinching the twine of the cell membrane near the equator of the cell, effectively separating the original cell
into two compartments, each containing a full set of unduplicated chromosomes. Reform the nuclear membranes around the chromosomes in
each cell compartment.

7. Illustrate cytokinesis by clipping the twine of the cell membrane and
reforming it into two distinct cells.

- *Scissors.*
- *Thin, flexible wire for use as microtubules.
  12 per student, cut to 10-cm lengths.*
- *Spools, small (2 per student) to symbolize
  centrioles. The "microtubule wire" (at least
  6 strands) should be wrapped around these.*

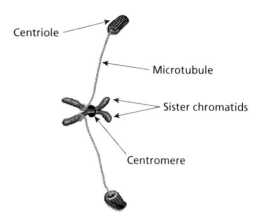

FIGURE 4.4

LAB EXERCISE 4.2

Hypothesizing About, and Estimating the Rate of, Cell Division

Materials:
* *Glass slides of onion root tip, 1 per student*
* *Compound microscopes*

We can estimate the rate of cell division in various tissues by microscopic examination of sections of this tissue stained to highlight the genetic material. Active growth in plants occurs at the tips of stems and roots. A simplified diagram of the growth regions of an onion root tip appears in Figure 4.5. The root cap functions to protect the actively growing regions of the root from the soil, while the apical meristem serves as the source of cells for mitosis.

A. Hypothesize about relative rate of cell division in various regions of an onion root tip.

Using the information provided in Figure 4.5 and the paragraph above, generate a hypothesis of the relative ranking of the rate of cell division in

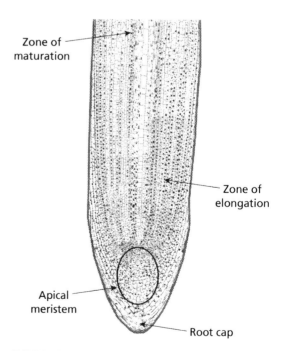

FIGURE 4.5

TABLE 4.1

Region of Root Tip	Relative Ranking of the Rate of Cell Division
Root Cap (large, slightly irregular cells)	
Apical Meristem (smaller, more tightly packed cells)	
Zone of Elongation (Larger, more rectangular cells)	
Zone of Maturation (Larger, more rectangular cells)	

the following regions of an onion root tip and record the information in Table 4.1. The ranking should be from 1 (fastest) to 4 (slowest).

B. Test your hypothesis by estimating the rate of cell division.

1. Work in groups of four students for this exercise.
2. Each student should examine the onion root tip slide provided under low-power magnification and generally identify the four regions described in the diagram. All of the members of the group should feel comfortable that your identification of these stages is correct. Ask your lab instructor for confirmation if necessary.
3. Assign one region to each student in your group. After you know the region for which you are estimating cell division rate, observe it under high-power magnification. In most regions, you should be able to see the square or rectangular cells and the genetic material within the cell. You might notice the linear chromosomes in various positions in some of the cells. These cells are somewhere in the process of mitosis. However, most cells will have an obvious nucleus with indistinctly stained genetic material, indicating that the chromosomes have not condensed.
4. Using the 40X objective, count all of the cells in a field of view, noting which are in the process of mitosis, and fill in Table 4.2. Repeat this for a total of three different fields of view for your assigned region. You

TABLE 4.2

Number of Cells in Stage	Interphase (Not Dividing)	Mitotic (Dividing)	Total Cells in View
View 1			
View 2			
View 3			
Total (1 + 2 + 3)			
Total Number Counted in Stage/ Total Cells Counted			
Percent of Cells in Each Stage (Previous Column × 100)			

might need to swap slides with another group member to provide enough different cells to observe.

Region of root tip examined: _____

5. Each student should enter his or her results in the appropriate row of Table 4.3. The relative rank of division rate is directly related to the percent of mitotic cells in each stage.

TABLE 4.3

Stage	Percent in Interphase	Percent Mitotic	Relative Rank of Division Rate
Root Cap			
Apical Meristem			
Zone of Elongation			
Zone of Maturation			

6. Compare your results to your hypothesis in part A. Were your predictions accurate? If not, why? Be prepared to share your results and discuss with your lab instructor and classmates.

(20 Minutes)

LAB EXERCISE 4.3

Evaluate the Relationship Between a Risk Factor and Cancer

Nearly 90% of the people who develop cancer do not have an inherited mutation that makes them especially susceptible to cancer; instead, they have *acquired* the crucial mutations throughout their lifetimes. Thus, there is enormous interest in identifying and controlling carcinogens in our environment. Epidemiologists face a difficult challenge when investigating the environmental causes of cancer. Because people are exposed to a diverse, and sometimes interacting, set of environmental conditions over their lifetimes, it can be difficult to demonstrate whether any single agent is carcinogenic. Read the following summary of the evidence for a relationship between second-hand smoke (also known as environmental tobacco smoke, or ETS) and cancer and answer the following set of questions. Be prepared to share your answers with your instructor and classmates.

- Active smoking is the principal cause of lung cancer. Exposure to ETS involves exposure to the same numerous carcinogens and toxic substances that are present in tobacco smoke produced by active smoking.
- More than 50 studies of ETS and lung cancer risk in people who have never smoked, especially spouses of smokers, have been published during the last 25 years. These studies have been carried out in many countries. Most showed an increased risk of lung cancer, especially for persons with higher exposures to ETS. The excess risk increases with increasing exposure.
- Experiments testing the carcinogenicity of ETS are typically performed on rodents. Machines that simulate human active smoking patterns by blowing smoke into the environment produce ETS for the animals. The experimental systems do not exactly simulate human exposures, and the tumors that develop in animals are not completely representative of human cancer.

A. Is this evidence sufficient to prove beyond a reasonable doubt that ETS causes lung cancer in humans? Why or why not?

Not really. The relationship between exposure to ETS and lung cancer in humans is established by correlation, which is always prone to the problem of alternative hypotheses. For example, nonsmokers exposed to high levels of ETS might be more likely to live in urban areas, and it might be some other environmental factor unique to urban areas that causes cancer. Animal studies also provide support for the hypothesis, but do not replicate the environmental conditions experienced by people—and animal models are imperfect "replacements" for people in experiments because of differences in biology and behavior.

B. What sort of evidence would be required to establish a cause and effect relationship between ETS and cancer in humans? Is this evidence likely to become available soon?

The strongest evidence would come from a controlled study in which participants and researchers were blind to the hypothesis and predicted outcomes. In other words, a study in which people were randomly assigned to "high ETS" and "low or no ETS" environments for many years, without knowing which environment they were in. This experiment is unlikely to ever happen, because it would require many years of exposure and unacceptable levels of control over people's actions during that time, as well as the morally questionable practice of intentionally exposing people to a suspected carcinogen to measure the results.

C. Given your answers to the previous two questions, explain why it is so difficult to prove a link between any environmental factor and an increased risk of cancer in humans.

Exposure to ETS is relatively easy to measure, based on smoking patterns of individuals in the primary environments of the subjects. Even given this, the link between ETS and lung cancer is strongly supported, but far from "fact." For many other chemicals, it is far more difficult to determine patterns and amount of exposure; for example, exposure to a particular pesticide results from exposure in areas where the pesticide is applied and contact with pesticide residues in water and food, both of which are difficult to measure after the fact.

D. People in industrialized countries are exposed to dozens, if not hundreds, of suspected carcinogens in the course of a year. We are also exposed to many other chemicals whose carcinogenic potential is unknown. And, new chemicals are produced and released into the environment continually. As a society, we potentially have three ways to address the environmental causes of cancer: 1) a new chemical is innocent until proven guilty—in other words, the chemical can be released widely with little restriction until science provides overwhelming evidence that the chemical causes cancer in the typical levels people are exposed to; 2) a new chemical is innocent until it appears guilty—the chemical can be released widely with little restriction until some evidence appears that it might cause cancer; 3) a new chemical is guilty until shown to be innocent—the chemical is highly restricted in use and release until studies indicate that the chemical is benign. Standards in the United States fall between option 1 and option 2. Do you think this is appropriate? Explain your answer.

E. Cancer has proven to be highly resistant to a cure. There are simply too many types of cancer and too many gene mutations that can lead to cancer to develop a one-size-fits-all cure. Despite many years and billions of dollars of research, cancer is still one of the leading causes of death in industrialized countries. Do you think more effort should be put into research on cancer prevention? Do you know what behaviors increase or decrease your cancer risk?

TOPIC 4
_____

POST-LABORATORY QUIZ

MITOSIS

1. A human cell contains 46 chromosomes. How many chromatids would be found in a cell at the beginning of mitosis?
   92

2. In this cell, the nuclear membrane has just disappeared and the chromosomes become visible as individual structures. Draw the cell at the next stage of mitosis.

3. During what stage of the cell cycle does DNA synthesis occur?
   Interphase

4. Describe what occurs during the anaphase of mitosis.
   Separation of sister chromatids to opposite poles of a dividing cell

5. What occurs during the process of cytokinesis after mitosis?
   The cell cleaves into two daughter cells, each with a complete set of chromosomes and surrounded by separate membranes.

6. Examine the following data in Table 4.4.

   TABLE 4.4

Tissue	% Cells in Interphase	% Cells Mitotic
Skin	75	25
Liver	90	10
Cornea	99	1

   Which tissue has the greatest rate of cell division?
   Skin

7. What is the significance of the line of duplicated chromosomes that forms at the cell's equator during metaphase of mitosis?
The line-up ensures that each daughter cell receives one copy of every chromosome.

8. What is cancer?
Uncontrolled growth of cells

9. Growth factors are proteins that stimulate cell division. Examine the data in Table 4.5:

TABLE 4.5

Cell Line	Growth Conditions	Behavior of Cells in Culture Dish
A	Nutrients	No mitosis
A	Nutrients + growth factor	Mitotic
B	Nutrients	No mitosis
B	Nutrients + growth factor	No mitosis
C	Nutrients	Mitotic
C	Nutrients + growth factor	Mitotic

Which of the cell lines is likely cancerous?
C

10. Dioxin, a by-product of the production of vinyl, is known to cause damage to DNA in cells in culture. How would an epidemiologist determine whether dioxin is a carcinogen?
Animal studies: Expose lab animals to different levels of dioxin and examine them for tumors.
Human studies: Examine large populations of people for correlations between dioxin exposure and various cancers.

TOPIC 5

Meiosis and Genetics

Learning Objectives

1. Describe how the process of meiosis relates to genetic inheritance.
2. Be able to relate an organism's genetic makeup to its physical appearance.
3. Define genotype, phenotype, homozygous, heterozygous, homologous pairs, alleles, meiosis, gametes, and fertilization.
4. Explain how Mendel's laws can be used to predict the outcomes of matings.
5. Understand that there are situations when Mendel's laws cannot predict the outcome of a mating.
6. Model the processes of meiosis and fertilization in an imaginary organism.
7. Be able to identify whether a trait is recessive, dominant, or codominant.

A pre-laboratory quiz is available in Appendix A on page 205.

Pre-laboratory Reading

All of us can think of traits that have been passed down in our own families. You might have hair color similar to your father, or eye shape similar to your mother; you also might worry that you have inherited the trait for an illness that is common among your relatives, such as heart disease or breast cancer. The study of the inheritance of traits is called **genetics**.

Traits are passed from one generation to the next when genes are passed from parents to offspring. Traits are passed on structures called chromosomes. Chromosomes are composed of a molecule called **deoxyribonucleic acid (DNA)** and a variety of proteins. Sections of DNA that encode traits are called **genes**. Each chromosome carries hundreds of genes. Figure 5.1 shows all of the chromosomes found in a human body cell. This picture is called a **karyotype**.

You can see from the karyotype that it is possible to arrange chromosomes into pairs. These pairs are called **homologous pairs**. Humans have 22 homologous pairs of chromosomes and one pair of **sex chromosomes**. Females have two X sex chromosomes, and males have one X and one Y sex chromosome.

Homologous pairs of chromosomes carry the same genes, but can carry different versions of each gene. Different versions of a gene are said to be **alleles** of a particular gene. Two individuals with different alleles of a gene will have different appearances or **phenotypes**. This is because an individual's phenotype is determined by the complement of alleles present, called the **genotype**.

Organisms pass their genes to their offspring via cells that are produced by a process of cell division called **meiosis**. In humans, meiosis occurs in the cells of the ovaries and testes to produce egg cells and sperm cells. Cells produced by meiosis are called **gametes** and they contain 1/2 of an individual's genes and chromosomes. Gametes are united at **fertilization**. When a gamete from a female fuses with a gamete from a male, genetic information from each parent will be present in the offspring.

Some genes that are passed on chromosomes are **dominant**, or expressed when there is one allele present, and some genes are **recessive**, or only expressed when two of the same alleles are present. An understanding of dominant and recessive interactions allows one to predict the outcomes of various crosses. In this lab, you will use imaginary organisms to help you understand the basic principles of genetics.

Autosomes (22 pairs)

Sex chromosomes (1 pair)

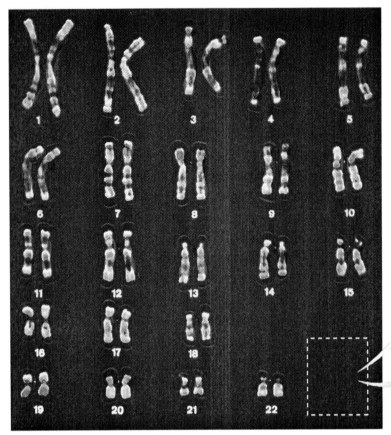

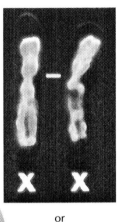

Female

or

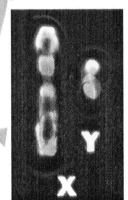

Male

FIGURE 5.1

(20 Minutes)

Materials:
- *Each group should have 6 pairs of pipe cleaners (chromosomes). Each pair should be composed of two pipe cleaners that are the same color. Therefore a total of 12 pipe cleaners are required. The pairs of chromosomes should be labeled as follows:*
- *Pair 1 should have one pipe cleaner labeled with a D and with an L. The other member of this pair should be labeled d and l.*
- *Pair 2 should have one pipe cleaner labeled Q and one labeled q.*
- *Pair 3 should have one pipe cleaner labeled E and one labeled e.*
- *Pair 4 should have one pipe cleaner labeled A and one labeled a.*
- *Pair 5 should have one pipe cleaner labeled M and one labeled m.*
- *Pair 6 should have one pipe cleaner labeled T and one labeled t.*
- *1 Mr. Potato Head doll per group*
- *Because there aren't enough parts for potato heads to have both a mustache and eyebrows, use black electrical tape for the eyebrows.*

LAB EXERCISE 5.1

From Genotype to Phenotype

A. Model chromosomes and phenotypes.

Examine the pile of pipe cleaner chromosomes on your lab table. As in a typical cell, these chromosomes are paired; that is, there are two of each type of chromosome. These pairs of chromosomes are homologous to each other. In this case, the members of a homologous pair are the same color. Note that all chromosomes are labeled with one or two letters. These letters are meant to represent a gene or genes that are located on that chromosome.

Because homologous pairs of chromosomes carry the same genes, both of the chromosomes in the pair should be labeled with the same letter or letters, although one may be uppercase and one lowercase. Uppercase and lowercase letters of a given gene represent different alleles of that gene.

Because genetic crosses using live organisms can require many weeks or months to produce offspring, we are going to use a model of a living organism to help illustrate the relationship between the information carried on chromosomes and the characteristics of an organism. Our model is Mr. Potato Head.

The chromosomes on your lab bench represent all of the chromosomes of Mr. Potato Head. Therefore, this assortment of chromosomes is what you would expect to find in one of his body cells. The letters on the chromosomes represent different alleles for various genetically determined traits. We are going to use the information in these genes to create our version of Mr. Potato Head.

1. The alleles for each gene on the chromosome on your table tell you what your Mr. Potato Head's genotype, or combination of alleles, is. Write his genotype here:

   Tt, _____, _____, _____, _____, _____, _____

   TtDdLlQqEeAaMm

2. An individual is said to be **homozygous** when he or she has two of the same alleles of a given gene and **heterozygous** when he or she has two different alleles of a given gene. Is Mr. Potato Head homozygous or heterozygous for each of the gene pairs in the preceding list?
   Heterozygous at all loci

3. Table 5.1 lists the relationship between the genotype of Mr. Potato Head and his phenotype. Use the Mr. Potato Head models at your lab bench to create the phenotype specified by the genotype present on your group's assortment of chromosomes.

TABLE 5.1

Genotype for Each Gene Pair	Phenotype
TT or Tt	Smiling
tt	Sticking out tongue
DD or Dd	Nose
dd	No nose
EE or Ee	Two ears
ee	No ears
MM	Eyebrows and mustache
Mm	Mustache only
mm	No facial hair
QQ	Hat only
Qq	Hat and shoes
qq	Shoes only
AA or Aa	Two arms
aa	No arms
LL or Ll	Eyes, but needs glasses
ll	Eyes, does not need glasses

4. Compare your Mr. Potato Head with others in class. You all started with the same genetic information in your hypothetical nondividing cell; therefore, all of the Potato Heads should have the same appearance. Do they?

They should all have the same appearance because they have the same genotype.

(30 Minutes)

Materials:
- *Copies of each pipe cleaner chromosome in a central location. You will need 6 additional pairs of pipe cleaners (with alleles labeled) per group.*
- *6 twist ties to represent centromeres*

LAB EXERCISE 5.2

From Parent to Offspring

Parents pass genes to their children by placing copies of their chromosomes into their gametes (eggs or sperm). Each normal gamete contains exactly half of the genetic information carried by the parent—thus each offspring has an equal number of genes from each parent. However, the half of each parent's genetic material that is passed on is not random. Each gamete contains one copy of every gene found in a human. In other words, each gamete contains one member of each homologous pair of chromosomes.

Recall that the process of cell division that produces gametes containing one homologue of each chromosome is called meiosis.

A. Model meiosis.

You will now model the parent cell represented by the chromosomes on your table undergoing meiosis to produce gametes. Use these instructions and Figure 5.2 as a guide.

1. Prior to meiosis, each chromosome must be replicated. This takes place during the portion of the cell cycle called **interphase**. Prior to this time, the chromosomes are stretched out and difficult to see under the microscope. To model replication, you should do the following:
   - Pick up from the center table a matching chromosome for each of the 12 chromosomes in the parent cell you started with.
   - Match each original chromosome with its replicate. These replicas are identical copies—each should carry the same allele. These identical copies are called **sister chromatids**. Note that this is really not the way that chromosome copies are produced—there are not extra chromosomes lying around in the cell. Instead, each chromosome is copied in place, and the two copies are held together at a structure called the **centromere**, which is analogous to a twist tie.
   - Clip the two copies together with the twist tie centromere. Now you have a representation of the chromosomes in Mr. Potato Head after they have replicated.

2. After interphase, the replicated chromosomes move into a phase of meiosis called **prophase I**. It is during prophase I that homologous pairs of chromosomes can undergo crossing-over. During the next step of meiosis, the homologous pairs of chromosomes move to the center of the cell. This occurs at the stage called **metaphase I**.
   - Line up the chromosomes as they appear at this stage of meiosis. Each chromosome is paired with its homologue, and members of a pair sit on opposite sides of an imaginary line that runs through the center of the cell, called the equator. (Note that the arrangement of each pair on this line is independent of the arrangement of the other pair. In other words, not all chromosomes carrying lowercase alleles have to be on one side of the cell.) This is called **random alignment** of the homologues.

3. At this point, the homologues separate and the parent cell divides into two daughter cells, each with only one type of each chromosome, although these chromosomes are still attached to their replicate. In Figure 5.2, these steps are labeled **anaphase I** and **telophase I**.

   • Separate each pair of homologues—place one homologue on one side of the table, the other homologue on the other side. Once separated, each cell begins another round of meiosis beginning with **prophase II**.

4. During **metaphase II** of meiosis, the chromosomes in each cell line up at the center of the cell. Model this for each daughter cell on different halves of your lab table. Unlike the first division, they are not paired, but form a single line across the equator.

5. The final division separates the identical copies of the chromosomes. This is illustrated in Figure 5.2 as **anaphase II** and **telophase II**. To model this, you will have to remove the centromere from each pair and place one copy in each of the four resulting daughter cells, now called gametes.

6. Check with your lab mates and/or instructor to determine whether you modeled meiosis correctly. Does each gamete have one of each type (that is, one of each color) of chromosome?

   Each gamete should have one member of each homologous pair, so six different colors of unclipped pipe cleaners should be present.

7. Every lab group started with the same chromosomes. Does everyone have identical gametes after meiosis? Why or why not?

   No. The assortment of alleles produced will be a function of the manner in which they were lined up at metaphase I (random alignment of the homologues).

8. How many genetically distinct kinds of gametes can be produced when six chromosomes each carry one gene with two different alleles? (To determine this mathematically, simply take the number of alleles (2) and raise it to the power of the number of chromosomes (6).)

   64

B. View meiosis.

1. View the prepared slides showing meiosis. What type of tissue is fixed to the slide?

   Varies

2. Why do you think this tissue type was used to display meiosis?

   Not all tissues undergo meiosis.

3. Try to identify a cell in each stage of meiosis.

Materials:

• *Prepared slides showing meiosis (available through Carolina Biological Supply or Tri-arch) You can select from slides of testis, ovary, anther, and so on. This can be set up prior to lab and students can view as a demonstration or students can attempt to find various stages of meiosis on their own prepared slide.*

LAB EXERCISE 5.3

Making Babies

(30 Minutes)

Suggestions: Answers to questions 3–8 will differ from group to group.

Now our Mr. Potato Heads are going to mate. The reproductive biology of Mr. Potato Head is still shrouded in mystery. Suffice it to say that they are able to mate among themselves, even though there appears to be only one gender.

A. Model fertilization.

1. Swap Mr. Potato Head gametes with a group of students at another lab table. Give them one of your gametes in exchange for one of theirs. Combine this new gamete with one of your remaining three gametes. This models the process of fertilization. The resulting cell should contain six homologous pairs of chromosomes. This offspring will be referred to as offspring A.

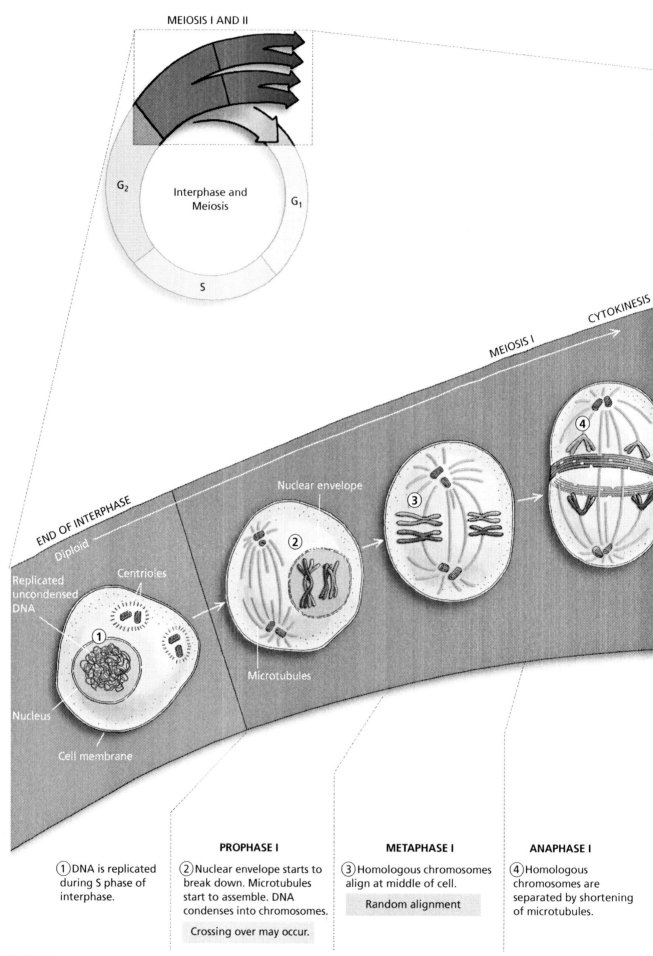

MEIOSIS I AND II

G_2

Interphase and Meiosis

G_1

S

CYTOKINESIS

MEIOSIS I

END OF INTERPHASE

Diploid

Nuclear envelope

Replicated uncondensed DNA

Centrioles

Microtubules

Nucleus

Cell membrane

PROPHASE I

METAPHASE I

ANAPHASE I

① DNA is replicated during S phase of interphase.

② Nuclear envelope starts to break down. Microtubules start to assemble. DNA condenses into chromosomes.

Crossing over may occur.

③ Homologous chromosomes align at middle of cell.

Random alignment

④ Homologous chromosomes are separated by shortening of microtubules.

FIGURE 5.2

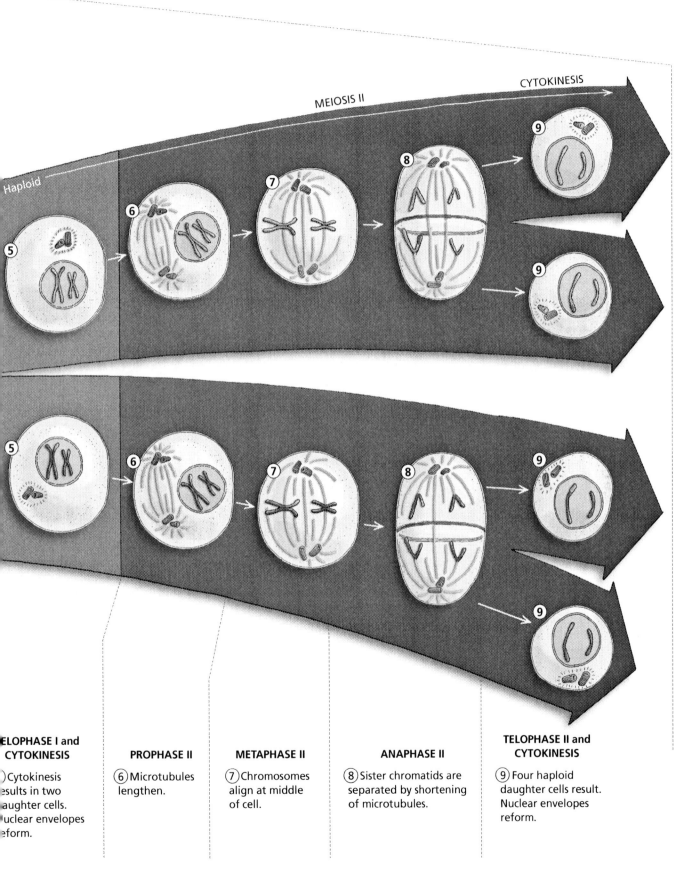

CYTOKINESIS

MEIOSIS II

Haploid

ΤΕLOPHASE I and CYTOKINESIS

⑤ Cytokinesis results in two daughter cells. Nuclear envelopes reform.

PROPHASE II

⑥ Microtubules lengthen.

METAPHASE II

⑦ Chromosomes align at middle of cell.

ANAPHASE II

⑧ Sister chromatids are separated by shortening of microtubules.

TELOPHASE II and CYTOKINESIS

⑨ Four haploid daughter cells result. Nuclear envelopes reform.

2. Repeat the process of fertilization with your remaining gametes with a group of students at another table to produce offspring B.
3. List the genotypes of the offspring:
   Offspring A:
   Offspring B:
4. List the phenotypes of the offspring in Tables 5.2 and 5.3. Consult Table 5.1 earlier in the chapter:

TABLE 5.2

Offspring A	
Mouth type	
Nose	
Ears	
Facial hair	
Clothing	
Arms	
Vision	

TABLE 5.3

Offspring B	
Mouth type	
Nose	
Ears	
Facial hair	
Clothing	
Arms	
Vision	

5. You will now produce grandchildren Potato Heads. Choose one of these offspring (A or B) to undergo meiosis again. Combine two of your four gametes with gametes from other groups. The offspring produced will be called offspring Y and offspring Z.
6. List the genotypes of these offspring:
   Offspring Y:
   Offspring Z:
7. List the phenotypes of these offspring in Tables 5.4 and 5.5.
8. Build Mr. Potato Heads representing both offspring Y and Z. Compare them with those your classmates made. The initial group of Potato Heads you made were all the same, yet they were able to produce many different-appearing offspring. Potato Heads have only one or two genes on each of 6 pairs of chromosomes. Humans have hundreds of genes on each of 23 pairs of chromosomes. Imagine the number of different offspring possible when humans mate. This explains why siblings can look very different from each other.

TABLE 5.4

Offspring Y	
Mouth type	
Nose	
Ears	
Facial hair	
Clothing	
Arms	
Vision	

TABLE 5.5

Offspring Z	
Mouth type	
Nose	
Ears	
Facial hair	
Clothing	
Arms	
Vision	

LAB EXERCISE 5.4

(30 Minutes)

Confirming Mendel's Ratios

Gregor Mendel, the founder of classical genetics, determined the nature of genes while studying inheritance in pea plants. Through careful **crossing** (mating) of the plants, Mendel noticed that traits appeared in offspring in consistent ratios. Mendel used the term **dominant** to refer to a trait that appeared whenever an individual had the gene for that trait, and **recessive** to refer to a trait that only appeared when the gene for the dominant trait was absent. When he crossed pea plants that were completely dominant against those that were completely recessive, he discovered that all of the offspring displayed the dominant trait. When he crossed these individuals, he found that their offspring displayed a ratio of three dominant for every one recessive. This result led him to conclude that individuals carry two copies of each gene and pass one copy of each gene to each of their offspring. (Actually, Mendel did not use the word gene—that is a more recent term).

A. Determine Mendelian expectations in crosses involving one gene.

1. Use the data from the whole class for offspring A and B to fill in Table 5.6.
2. Did this trait generally conform to Mendelian expectations?
   Yes

TABLE 5.6

Group #	# Smiling	# Sticking Tongue Out
1		
2		
3		
4		
5		
6		
Total Number		
Ratio		

B. Determine Mendelian expectations in crosses involving two genes.

When Mendel observed the inheritance of two different characters, he discovered that, at least for the traits he examined, genes are inherited independently of each other. In other words, two traits that occurred together in a plant (such as tall height and white flowers) might not be found together in the second generation of a cross between two different plants. When he examined the ratios of these crosses, he discovered that among the second-generation offspring, for every one individual displaying both recessive traits, there were nine individuals displaying both dominant traits, three displaying the recessive trait for one character and the dominant trait for the other, and three displaying the converse.

1. Use the data from offspring A and B to fill in Table 5.7.

TABLE 5.7

Group #	Two Ears, Nose	Two Ears, No Nose	No Ears, Nose	No Ears, No Nose
1				
2				
3				
4				
5				
6				
Total				
Ratio				

2. Does the ratio generally conform to Mendel's expected 9:3:3:1 pattern? If it doesn't, why not?
   Should be close. If off, it's due to small sample size.

C. Examine the phenotypic ratio for another pair of genes.

1. Use offspring Y and Z to fill in Table 5.8.

2. Do the phenotypes for these genes conform to the expected 9:3:3:1 ratio? Why or why not?
   All except D and L should give the 9:3:3:1 ratio.

TABLE 5.8

Group #	Nose, Glasses	Nose, No Glasses	No Nose, Glasses	No nose, No Glasses
1				
2				
3				
4				
5				
6				
Total				
Ratio				

3. Look closely at the ratios produced for genes D and L. These two genes are linked to each other; that is, they are found on the same chromosome. Do genes that are linked to each other assort independently? Why or why not?

   No, because random alignment is not possible.

4. Look at the genotype/phenotype relationship for gene Q. Is one allele dominant to the other?

   No, Q codes for hat and q codes for shoes. If Q were dominant to q, the presence of a hat would mask the presence of shoes.

   When both alleles of a gene are expressed (versus one allele being dominant over the other), we say that the alleles of a gene are **codominant** to each other.

5. Look at the genotype/phenotype relationship for gene M. Is one allele dominant to the other? Explain.

   No, one dominant allele gives facial hair and two dominants gives facial and eyebrow hair.

   Instead of simulating meiosis and fertilization using pipe cleaners, scientists make use of a tool called a Punnett square. By listing the gametes produced by the male parent on one axis and the gametes produced by the female parent on the other axis, and then combining the gametes to produce offspring in the middle of the Punnett square, scientists can make predictions about the kinds of offspring two parents can produce together.

6. Represent the cross between your offspring Z and your neighbor's for gene E with a Punnett square.

7. Make a second Punnett square representing the cross between your offspring Z and your neighbor's for genes D and T.

TOPIC 5 _____

POST-LABORATORY QUIZ

MEIOSIS AND GENETICS

1. Define the terms genotype and phenotype.
   Genotype is the combination of alleles. Phenotype is the physical appearance.

2. Are the following genotypes homozygous or heterozygous?
   A. AA
   B. Aa
   C. aa

   > *AA = homozygous*
   > *Aa = heterozygous*
   > *aa = homozygous*

3. Draw a homologous pair of chromosomes before replication. Depict each member of the pair carrying different alleles of gene A.
   Students should draw two linear chromosomes, one carrying an A allele and one carrying an a allele.

4. Draw two homologous pairs of chromosomes after replication. Draw one homologous pair as heterozygous for gene A and the other as homozygous for gene B. Label the sister chromatids and homologous pairs.
   Students should draw four X-shaped chromosomes. Each sister chromatid of one member of the A homologous pair should be labeled with a capital A, the others with a lowercase a. The two members of the B pair should be labeled with capital Bs.

5. What kinds of gametes can be produced by a parent with the genotype WWXXYyZZ?
   WXYZ and WXyZ

6. In humans, the gene for tongue rolling (R) is dominant over its allele for nonrolling (r). A man, homozygous for tongue rolling, marries a woman who cannot roll her tongue. Predict the phenotypes and genotypes of any offspring produced from this mating.
   Rr (rollers)

7. In peas, tall (TT) is dominant over short (tt). Three experiments in cross-pollination gave the following results. In each case, give the *most probable* genotype for each parent.

   A. tall x tall produced 95 tall, 29 short
      Tt × Tt

   B. tall x short produced 50 tall, 0 short
      TT × tt

   C. tall x tall produced 75 tall, 0 short
      TT × TT or TT × Tt

8. In peas, the gene for smooth seed coat (S) is dominant to the one for wrinkled seeds (s). What would be the genotypic and phenotypic results of the following matings:

   A. heterozygous smooth x heterozygous smooth?
      1 SS (smooth): 2 Ss (smooth): 1 ss (wrinkled)

   B. heterozygous smooth x wrinkled?
      1 Ss (smooth): 1 ss (wrinkled)

   C. wrinkled x wrinkled?
      All ss (wrinkled)

9. Predict the phenotypic ratios from the following cross: AaBb x AaBb.
   9:3:3:1
   9 A-B-; 3 A-bb; 3 aaB-; 1 aabb

10. Can you design a cross involving two genes that would not lead to the ratio you predicted in the previous question?
    AABB x aabb or Aabb x aabb, and so on

TOPIC 6

DNA Structure, Synthesis, and Fingerprinting

Learning Objectives

1. Explain how DNA is extracted from living cells and describe its texture and appearance.
2. Describe the molecular structure of DNA.
3. Understand and model the process of semiconservative DNA replication.
4. Understand how DNA fingerprinting can be used to identify individuals.

A pre-laboratory quiz is available in Appendix A on page 207.

Pre-laboratory Reading

The DNA molecule is the molecule of heredity that is passed from parents to offspring. Figure 6.1 shows this molecule's structure.

The DNA molecule is composed of two strands. Each strand has a backbone made up of a sugar, **deoxyribose**, and a phosphate group. The backbone holds the strand together, but does not contain any genetic information. The alignment of the two strands of a DNA molecule is referred to as **antiparallel**. In other words, the backbones are flipped with respect to each other.

In addition to the sugar-phosphate backbone, the DNA molecule contains chemicals called **nitrogenous bases**. The nitrogenous bases found in DNA include adenine (A), cytosine (C), guanine (G), and thymine (T). Different DNA molecules have different orders of nitrogenous bases.

The nitrogenous bases are connected to the backbone via the sugar molecule, which in turn, is connected to a phosphate group. When taken together, the nitrogenous base, the sugar, and the phosphate are called a **nucleotide**. Different nucleotides in DNA have different nitrogenous bases connected to the sugar molecule.

The nitrogenous bases of the two strands pair with each other according to the **base pairing rules**: A always bonds with T, and G always bonds with C. Bonds between bases hold the two strands of the molecule together. These **hydrogen bonds** are symbolized by dotted lines because they are weaker than typical chemical bonds and are more easily broken.

It is relatively straightforward for a cell to copy its DNA because the parental DNA molecule can be used as a template for the synthesis of new, so-called daughter strands. The parental strand is unwound and new nucleotides are added according to the base pairing rules.

DNA can be used as a molecular identification tag when subjected to the process of DNA fingerprinting. This is based on the fact that different people will always, unless they are identical twins, have different DNA sequences.

In this laboratory, you will examine real DNA molecules, make a three-dimensional model DNA, and then manipulate the model to understand DNA synthesis and DNA fingerprinting.

(a) DNA double helix is made of two strands.

(b) Each strand is a chain of of antiparallel nucleotides.

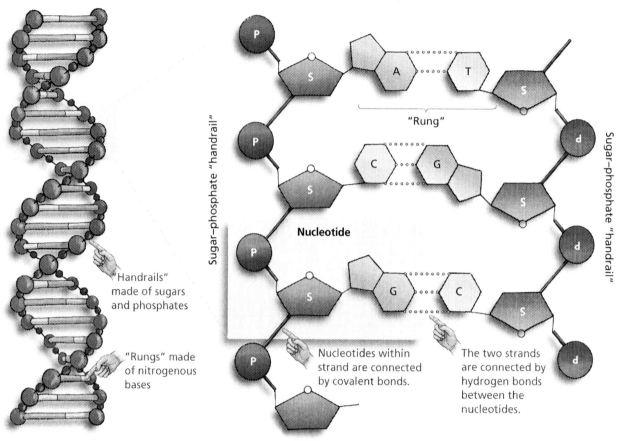

Sugar-phosphate "handrail"

Sugar-phosphate "handrail"

"Rung"

Nucleotide

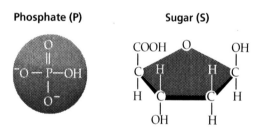

"Handrails" made of sugars and phosphates

"Rungs" made of nitrogenous bases

Nucleotides within strand are connected by covalent bonds.

The two strands are connected by hydrogen bonds between the nucleotides.

(c) Each nucleotide is composed of a phosphate, a sugar, and a nitrogenous base.

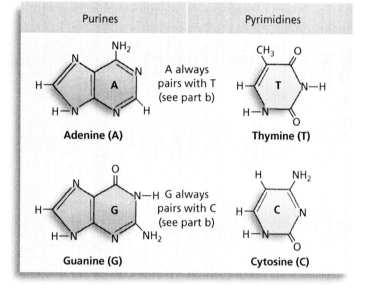

Phosphate (P)

Sugar (S)

Deoxyribose

Nitrogenous bases

Purines	Pyrimidines
Adenine (A)	Thymine (T)
Guanine (G)	Cytosine (C)

A always pairs with T (see part b)

G always pairs with C (see part b)

FIGURE 6.1

LAB EXERCISE 6.1

Extract and Examine DNA from Living Cells

With a few exceptions, all cells contain the entire DNA sequence of an individual. DNA molecules are surprisingly easy to extract from cells. In this exercise, you will examine DNA extracted from your own body cells.

A. Examine and collect cheek cells.

The lining of your mouth, especially of the cheeks, is made up of cells that are continually being sloughed off and replaced.

1. Examine a slide of cheek cells under a microscope. Draw a picture of a few cells below. Where is the DNA contained in these cells?
   Inside the nucleus

2. Pour 10 mL (about 2 teaspoons) of 0.9% salt water into a small paper cup. Vigorously swish the water in your mouth for 30 seconds. The more you swish, the more DNA in your dish! After swishing, spit the water back into the cup.

B. Break open the cells.

The cleaning action of most dish soaps comes from sodium lauryl sulfate. This chemical breaks up large globs of grease (fat), allowing it to be washed away by water. The membranes of cells contain phospholipids, a type of fat. The membranes of cells exposed to high concentrations of sodium lauryl sulfate dissolve, releasing the contents of the cell into solution.

1. Add the water from the cup to a test tube containing 1 mL (about 1/4 teaspoon) of liquid dish detergent. Cap the tube.

2. Gently rock the test tube back and forth for 2–3 minutes, in order to break up the cell membranes. Vigorous shaking will break the DNA molecules, making them more difficult to see.

C. Separate and remove the DNA from the solution.

1. Open the tube and tilt it slightly. Gently pour 5 mL (1 teaspoon) of ice-cold 95% ethanol down the side of the tube so that it forms a layer on top of the solution. Do not mix! Let stand for 1 minute.

   The DNA will precipitate at the boundary between the solution and the alcohol. After a minute or so, you should begin to see a cloudy layer at this boundary.

2. Take a glass rod or paper clip and twirl it slowly, in one direction, through this boundary layer. The DNA should begin to wind around the rod.

   What does the DNA look like? How does it feel? (If you do touch the DNA, be sure to wash your hands thoroughly afterwards).

(20 minutes)

Materials:
- *Prepared slide, cheek (buccal) cells. Note: Instructors can make a slide of cheek cells for the whole class to view, or students can make their own. Take a toothpick and scrape the inside of a cheek, then transfer the material to a slide. Take a cover slip and smear the material across the slide. Allow to air dry. Flood with a few drops of methylene blue and cover with the cover slip.*
- *1 per student: small paper cups, small test tubes with caps (centrifuge tubes work well), glass stirring rod*
- *Per class of 24: 250 mL 0.9% sodium chloride solution (20 g NaCl, 250 mL water) in a perfectly clean, sterilized container. 10-mL graduated cylinder, dedicated to this solution. Again, this must be clean and sterilized—students will be putting the NaCl solution in their mouths.*
- *Liquid dish detergent containing sodium laurel sulfate (most do, but check)*
- *$\frac{1}{4}$ teaspoon for measuring the detergent (can use a graduated cylinder, but a teaspoon is easier)*
- *250 mL of ice-cold 95% ethanol*
- *Alternatives to cheek cells: almost anything. Raw wheat germ (about 1 gram per protocol) works very well and produces lots of DNA. One reviewer also suggests fresh or frozen strawberries.*

Are you surprised that this substance contains all the genetic information needed to build you?

Are you surprised that your DNA was so easy to extract? What sorts of information could we collect from this DNA? Does it concern you that it is so easy to get?

(20 Minutes)

LAB EXERCISE 6.2

Constructing a 3-D Model of DNA

Materials:
- *Note cards or printed paper strips with 45 nucleotides listed. Use the sequence ID numbers as listed in Appendix B, page 233. The justification for these codes (that is, M1) will be explained in Laboratory Exercise 6.4. If they all have sequences beginning with the same ID letter, four students at a standard lab table can create, in aggregate, a DNA molecule for a single individual.*
- *Thin wire or twine for the backbone and 4 different-colored beads to represent 4 nucleotides. When purchasing wire twine, obtain two different colors. Use one color for parental molecules and another for daughter molecules in Exercise 6.3. The beads should have holes through the center. Each hole should be large enough to accommodate the twine. You will need enough beads for each student to make his or her DNA sequence and for each student to replicate the sequence in a later exercise. (You might want to look ahead to Topic 7, which also requires some beads, to save a trip to the bead store.) If you don't want to use beads, it is also possible to use photocopies of drawings of the four nucleotides. Keep these photocopies small so the students can string long stretches together.*

A. Building DNA

Obtain a note card bearing a printed DNA sequence from your lab instructor. This is a list of the nucleotide bases from one strand of a segment of DNA molecule. Note that this is a very short strand—in humans most chromosomes contain around 100 million bases!

1. Note the sequence ID# here: _____
2. Keep track of which nucleotide each colored bead represents in Table 6.1.

TABLE 6.1

NUCLEOTIDE	COLOR
A	
C	
G	
T	

3. Use the wire and beads provided to build a 3-D double-stranded model of this DNA strand. The twine represents the backbone (sugars and phosphates) and the four different-colored beads represent the four nitrogenous bases (A, C, G, T). Once you have created the double-stranded molecule, twist it to produce the three-dimensional helix structure.

(20 Minutes)

LAB EXERCISE 6.3

DNA Replication

Materials: DNA strands just synthesized by students, and enough beads and a second color of twine to replicate them.
Instructors: Students may complain that this exercise is tedious, especially if assigned after the previous exercise. We have made it into a game in our labs by having students "race" against each other to complete the task. In

DNA replication occurs in the nuclei of your cells prior to the process of cell division. In an earlier laboratory, you practiced the process of meiosis, the division that, in humans, results in the production of gametes called sperm and egg cells. The gametes produced by meiosis carry their own unique complement of genetic information.

Mitosis is the type of cell division that produces genetically identical daughter cells. Mitosis takes place in all of our cells except for the testes or ovaries. Producing genetically identical copies is fairly straightforward for cells because of the complementary nature of the two DNA strands.

One of the enzymes that facilitates DNA replication functions by first unwinding the DNA molecule. This unwinding occurs as the hydrogen bonds holding nitrogenous bases are broken. Once unwound, each strand of the DNA molecule can be used as a template for the synthesis of a new daughter strand of DNA. **DNA polymerase** is the enzyme that joins adjacent nucleotides to each other. Figure 6.2 illustrates the process of DNA replication.

A. Use the double-stranded DNA molecule you made in the previous laboratory exercise as a template for the synthesis of two new daughter DNA molecules. Do this by first unwinding the double-stranded DNA and then following the rules of complementarity to make newly synthesized daughter DNA strands. Use a different color of twine when synthesizing the daughter DNA molecules.

addition to energizing students, it can provide an interesting teaching point about the trade-off in DNA replication between speed and accuracy. In general, DNA polymerases that work fast (such as those in bacteria) are more error prone than those that work a little more slowly (such as those in humans).

You may wish to save the double-stranded DNA molecules for use in the Topic 7 lab.

(a) DNA replication

(b) The DNA polymerase enzyme facilitates replication.

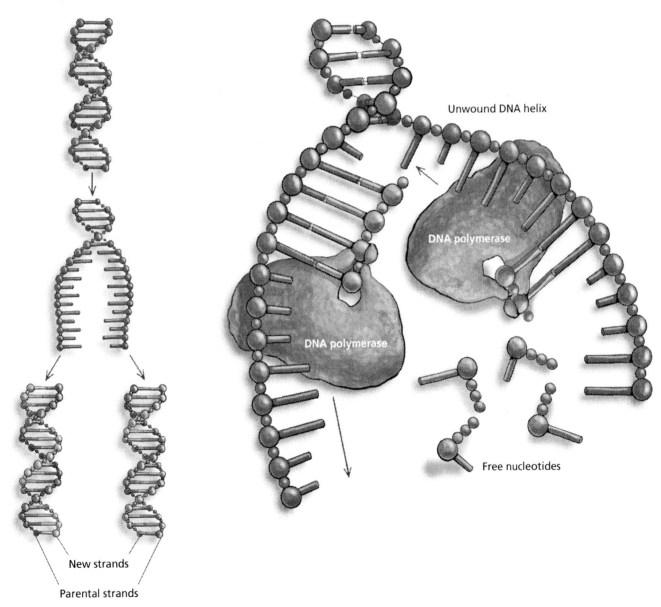

Unwound DNA helix

DNA polymerase

DNA polymerase

Free nucleotides

New strands

Parental strands

FIGURE 6.2

B. Describe the daughter DNA molecules you produced in terms of their origin. Are they composed of all daughter DNA, all parental DNA, or some parental DNA and some daughter DNA?

1/2 parental DNA and 1/2 daughter DNA

DNA synthesis is sometimes referred to as **semiconservative** replication because each daughter strand is composed of half parental DNA and half newly synthesized daughter DNA. In other words, half of the original parental DNA molecule is conserved in each daughter molecule.

C. Show your instructor the daughter DNA molecules you have made to be certain you made them correctly, and then disassemble one of them.

Note that replication is the point at which changes to the DNA sequence, called **mutations**, can occur. Errors are relatively rare, but the human genome contains over six billion bases—so even with a very low error rate, each round of replication can potentially result in mutations.

(30 Minutes)

Materials:
- *The students use either the 3-D DNA sequence they created in Lab Exercise 6.2 or a photocopy of the DNA sequences from Appendix B, page 233. The coding works as follows: Any sequence labeled "M#" is mom, "P#" is puppy, and the rest are possible fathers. The sequences will be lined up in numerical order—for example, M1, M2, M3, M4—to give the whole genome for an individual.*
- *Scissors*

LAB EXERCISE 6.4

DNA Fingerprinting

A. Understanding the basics of DNA structure and replication can help you understand how DNA is manipulated to create DNA fingerprints. In this lab exercise, you will use the DNA sequences you assembled to determine the paternity of a dog.

1. Find the sequence ID for your genetic sequence on the first page of this lab. Everyone in your lab group should have a sequence ID with the same first letter.

2. Link the DNA sequences end to end in numerical order according to their sequence ID (for example, M1, M2, M3, M4). This is your lab group's chromosome. Chromosomes are not this short, of course, and in most species, chromosomes contain a lot of DNA that does not code for genes, but this model will work for our next exercise.

   A DNA fingerprint is a unique pattern of DNA fragments that results when an individual's unique DNA is chopped up by chemicals called **restriction enzymes**. These enzymes cut DNA at specific sequences. The restriction enzyme we will use in our simulation is *Ham*III, which cuts DNA wherever the sequence GGCC is found (on either strand). Thus, in a DNA molecule:

   – – – GG | CC– – – CC | GG– – – (dashes indicate other bases)
   – – – CC | GG– – – GG | CC– – –

   the restriction enzyme cuts at the point marked by the vertical lines, resulting in three DNA fragments of different lengths.

3. Examine your table's chromosome. Use the scissors provided to cut the DNA molecule at every *Ham*III restriction site.

4. Visually represent the fragments that result as follows:

   a. Count the total number of bases (on both strands of the DNA molecule) that make up each fragment.

   b. Find your "lane" on the following table and draw lines in the lane that correspond to the length of each fragment. This is your chromosomes' fingerprint.

TABLE 6.2   **DNA Fingerprints**

Fragment Size	M	P	W	X	Y	Z
150						
145						
140						
135						
130						
125						
120						
115						
110						
105						
100						
95						
90						
85						
80						
75						
70						
65						
60						
55						
50						
45						
40						
35						
30						
25						
20						
15						
10						

5. Visit the other tables to collect their fingerprints and fill in the appropriate lane in Table 6.2.

What you have just drawn is equivalent to the DNA fingerprint produced by a forensics laboratory. In a real DNA fingerprint, the fragments are separated from each other by size according to how quickly they move through a gelatinous substance called a gel. DNA has a slight negative charge, and it will be attracted to a positive charge. To separate the fragments, the chopped-up DNA is placed on one side of the gel and the fragments are then subjected to an electric current. As the fragments migrate through the gel toward the charge, the larger fragments move more slowly than smaller fragments because the gel impedes the progress of the larger ones more than the smaller ones. Over time, the distance between fragments of different sizes grows.

The American Kennel Club (AKC) has a DNA profiling program to help breeders determine the correct sire (father) of a litter of puppies. The DNA fingerprints you just produced provide an illustration of how these profiles can be used to determine the paternity of a puppy whose parentage is unclear. The puppy's fingerprint is in lane P. The dam (mother) of this puppy is known, and her fingerprint is in lane M. Because the puppy's entire DNA was inherited from its mother and father, any DNA fragment possessed by the puppy must be present in one of his or her parents. Thus, the father of this puppy is the one with the fragments that fill in the gaps—the DNA fragments it could not have received from its mother. Since the DNA fingerprints of approved sires are kept on record in the AKC's database, the puppy's father can be clearly identified.

6. Which fingerprint—W, X, Y, or Z—belongs to this puppy's sire?

TOPIC 6
_____

POST-LABORATORY QUIZ

DNA STRUCTURE, SYNTHESIS, AND FINGERPRINTING

1. What technique do researchers use to access a cell's DNA?

   Mix the cell in a solution containing detergent, which disrupts the cell and nuclear membranes, releasing the DNA.

2. If one strand of a DNA molecule has the sequence AGCTTCAGT, the other strand should have the sequence:

   TCGAAGTCA

3. List the components of a nucleotide. Which of these differ between different nucleotides?

   Sugar, phosphate, nitrogenous base: nitrogenous base.

4. Using two differently colored pencils (or a pen and a pencil), diagram a double-stranded DNA molecule undergoing replication. Start with two intertwined lines of one color representing the parental DNA molecule. Diagram the results of two rounds of semiconservative DNA replication using the second color to represent the daughter DNA.

5. Why are chromosomes sometimes depicted as linear structures and sometimes as Xs?

   Linear = unduplicated; X = duplicated

6. Why might DNA fingerprinting be more useful in identifying individuals than blood typing analysis?

   Fingerprinting provides unique identification versus blood typing, which can only be used to exclude individuals. Just because a man has the same blood type as a child does not mean the man fathered the child. Likewise, the fact that a child has a blood type that is consistent with those the man could have produced does not guarantee that the man is the father.

7. What do we call mistakes in DNA replication that are passed on to offspring?
   Mutations

8. If a DNA fingerprint from a suspect matches blood found at the scene of a crime, should the suspect be convicted?
   Maybe, but we can't know why the blood was there. Other information learned at trial must be considered.

9. Why might two related individuals share more similar DNA fingerprints than unrelated individuals?
   Related individuals share more DNA sequences because they have a common ancestor who passed genes to both of them.

10. What biological molecules act as molecular scissors to cut DNA at specific locations?
    Restriction enzymes

TOPIC 7

Transcription, Translation, and Genetically Modified Organisms

Learning Objectives

1. Understand and model the process of transcription.
2. Understand and model the process of translation.
3. Model the effects of a mutation on protein shape and function.
4. Explore how gene expression is regulated in bacteria.
5. Participate in a debate about genetically modified organisms.

A pre-laboratory quiz is available in Appendix A on page 209.

Pre-laboratory Reading

During the previous laboratory sessions, you learned about DNA structure and replication. During today's laboratory session, you will explore the significance of differences in DNA sequences. Sequences of DNA that code for the production of proteins are called **genes**. A gene can be thought of as a set of instructions for the assembly of a protein.

Proteins are produced by the stepwise processes of **transcription** and **translation**.

During the process of transcription (see Figure 7.1), the DNA comprising a gene is used as a template in the production of a molecule called **RNA (ribonucleic acid)**. RNA differs from DNA in that the sugar is **ribose** (not deoxyribose) and instead of the nucleotide thymine, there are **uracils (U)**. The RNA produced by transcription is called **messenger RNA (mRNA)** because it carries the message from the DNA. These mRNA transcripts are single-stranded.

The production of the mRNA molecule from the DNA template strand requires the help of an enzyme called **RNA polymerase**. This enzyme ties together adjacent RNA nucleotides as they are being added to the growing mRNA transcript. The transcript is produced when complementary base pairs

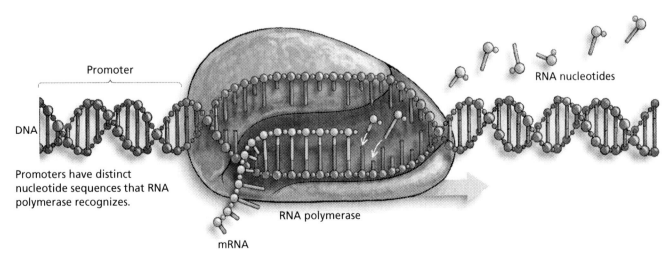

Promoter

RNA nucleotides

DNA

Promoters have distinct
nucleotide sequences that RNA
polymerase recognizes.

RNA polymerase

mRNA

FIGURE 7.1

transiently form with the DNA template strand. RNA makes base pairs with DNA according to the rules listed in Table 7.1.

TABLE 7.1   **DNA:RNA Base-Pairing Rules**

DNA	: RNA
C	: G
G	: C
A	: U
T	: A

After the mRNA is produced by transcription, its message is decoded and a protein is produced by the process of translation (see Figure 7.2).

Translation occurs in the cytoplasm of cells on structures called **ribosomes**. Ribosomes help anchor the mRNA and help synthesize the protein coded for in the DNA. The mRNA is "read" or deciphered by the ribosome as a series of three nucleotides called **codons**. Each codon specifies the incorporation of a given amino acid. Scientists can determine which amino acid a particular codon codes for by finding the codon on a chart called the **Genetic Code** (see Table 7.2).

Overall, the sequence of bases in the DNA is transcribed into the complementary sequence of bases in the mRNA. When the mRNA is threaded through the ribosome, the exposed codons dictate which amino acids will be incorporated into the protein the gene encodes.

TABLE 7.2

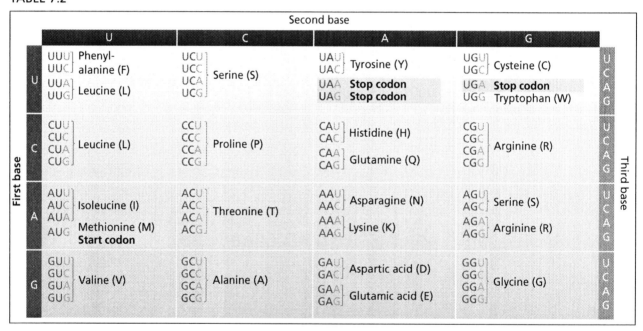

Nearly all organisms, from bacteria and fungi to plants and humans, incorporate the same amino acid in response to the same codon. Therefore, two mRNA molecules that carry the same protein-building instructions will be translated to produce the same proteins in two different organisms. Because of this essential universality of the Genetic Code, bacteria can be used to pro-

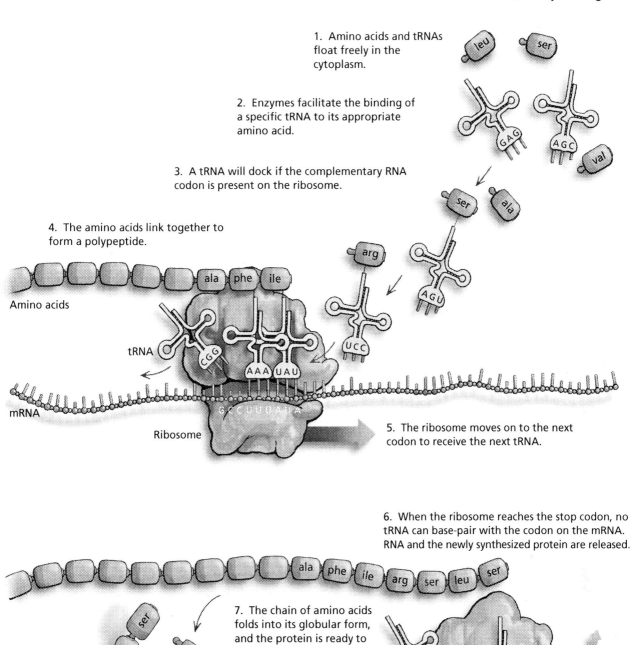

1. Amino acids and tRNAs float freely in the cytoplasm.

2. Enzymes facilitate the binding of a specific tRNA to its appropriate amino acid.

3. A tRNA will dock if the complementary RNA codon is present on the ribosome.

4. The amino acids link together to form a polypeptide.

Amino acids

tRNA

mRNA

Ribosome

5. The ribosome moves on to the next codon to receive the next tRNA.

6. When the ribosome reaches the stop codon, no tRNA can base-pair with the codon on the mRNA. RNA and the newly synthesized protein are released.

7. The chain of amino acids folds into its globular form, and the protein is ready to perform its job.

Protein

8. The subunits of the ribosome separate but can reassemble and begin translation of another mRNA.

FIGURE 7.2

duce human proteins; plants can produce bacterial proteins, and so on. When an organism is genetically engineered to contain foreign DNA so that it can produce a protein that it would not normally produce, it is said to be a **genetically modified organism (GMO)**.

(25 Minutes)

Materials:
The 45-nucleotide DNA strands students built and saved from Lab Topic 6. If you did not use Topic 6, you will need the sequences from page 233 of Appendix B. These sequences represent the coding strand of a DNA molecule. Students will also need beads and twine to make mRNA. If possible, the beads should be shaped or colored differently than the beads used for DNA synthesis, or the backbone twine or wire should be a different color, to illustrate that the sugar is different in RNA.

LAB EXERCISE 7.1

Modeling Transcription

You can think of the information for protein production, which is stored in a DNA molecule, as equivalent to recipes in a cookbook—the recipe is not the food, but the directions for making the food. If you want to eat the dish described, you have to translate words of the recipe into actions.

Transcription of a gene is the first step in converting the information stored in a DNA molecule into a structure that will affect an organism's biology. Using our recipe book analogy, transcribing DNA is a lot like copying a single recipe from a large cookbook onto an index card before you make the dish. Although most cooks probably don't do this, they might if the recipe book was very rare and they wanted to avoid spilling on it, or if the book was enormous and would crowd out all the work space on their counters. The cell transcribes DNA for both of these reasons—the DNA needs to be shielded from damage and it is a huge, unwieldy molecule.

A recently made transcript is a copy of a single gene whose product the cell currently requires. In human cells, this transcript moves out of the nucleus (where the DNA is stored) and into the cytoplasm where it will be translated.

Look at the double-stranded DNA sequence you have been given. This sequence contains the information from a single gene. A sequence of nucleotides on one strand of the DNA double helix serves as a molecular signal that tells the RNA polymerase that this is the beginning of a gene. This sequence of bases serves as a binding site for the RNA polymerase and is called the **promoter**.

Human cells have a promoter at the beginning of each and every gene. The RNA polymerase actually recognizes a sequence of bases in the promoter called the **TATA box**. The term TATA box is an abbreviation for the actual sequence of bases in the promoter to which the RNA polymerase binds, which is TATAAA.

A. Locate the TATA box at the beginning of your gene. The strand of DNA that this sequence is found on is called the **coding strand**. The parallel strand is thus called the **non-coding strand**. RNA polymerase creates a complementary sequence to the non-coding strand, thus producing an RNA version of the coding strand.

B. For most genes, transcription begins several nucleotides "downstream" (or down the strand) from the TATA box. In this case, we will assume that transcription begins with the first nucleotide after the TATAAA box. List the sequence of the mRNA that would be produced. You can determine this sequence like RNA polymerase does, by listing the RNA complement of the non-coding strand, or you can take a shortcut by writing an RNA version of the coding strand (i.e. replacing the T's with U's). Create this RNA sequence out of beads.
Varies depending on sequence ID

C. The beads representing the RNA nucleotides differ from those representing DNA. Why did you use different beads to represent A, C, and G when making your mRNA transcript?
Sugar differs

LAB EXERCISE 7.2

Modeling Translation

The second step in deciphering the code of a DNA sequence is to translate the information from the transcript into a physical structure. The structures coded for by most genes are **proteins**. Proteins are complex chemicals that comprise the majority of a cell's dry weight. Proteins have many and varied functions. They function inside of cells as enzymes and as structural components of cells. They also help transport other substances into and out of cells.

Regardless of their function, proteins are composed of various amino acids joined to each other. Individual amino acids are joined together to produce a given protein on structures called ribosomes. For this reason, ribosomes are often referred to as the workbenches of the cell. By using the Genetic Code, you can determine the amino acid called for by a given 3-base codon. The Genetic Code is a chart that shows the relationship between the information on the mRNA transcript (or the DNA coding strand it mirrors) and the sequence of amino acids in a protein. The relationship between codon and amino acid is illustrated in Table 7.2.

Note that there is one **start codon** (AUG). This sequence should be present at the beginning of every mRNA. There are also three codons that do not code for amino acids; instead, these codons signal the end of one protein coding sequence and are called **stop codons**.

A. What amino acid will all proteins made in this modeling exercise begin with?

   Methionine

B. What sequences make-up the three stop codons?

   UAA, UAG, and UGA

C. Use the Genetic Code, the blocks representing amino acids, and the string to create a sequence of amino acids that corresponds to your DNA segment. List the amino acid sequence of your protein.

   Differs

D. Every student at your table received a genetic sequence 39 bases long (after the TATA box). How many amino acids could the protein specified by this sequence contain?

   13

E. How many does yours contain?

   Differs

F. Why is there sometimes a difference between the maximum and actual number?

   Stop codons

(25 Minutes)

Materials:
To make the proteins, use blocks from a craft store that can be labeled with single-letter amino acid abbreviations. Students can connect these together on thin craft wire. You will need one block for each amino acid coded for in the sequences you hand out (13 × the number of sequences). It is also possible to use photocopies of the different amino acids for this lab exercise. Keep the photocopies small so students can string a number of them together to produce their protein.

Some users of this manual have used sets of magnetic blocks sold in toy stores. Sets that come with six different colors of magnets allow users to classify amino acids; for example, all blue magnets are hydrophilic, all yellow magnets are hydrophobic. The magnets can be labeled with permanent marker or labeling tape.

Other users of this lab manual have had success using a Science Kit/Boreal Laboratories product called "Protein Modeling Toobers." A set of 10 models is available from this company for $60.

(All proteins don't actually begin with this amino acid. It is often cleaved out after protein synthesis.)

LAB EXERCISE 7.3

Protein Folding and Mutations

(20 Minutes)

After a protein is translated, it folds into a more globular structure than a string because of attraction and repulsion of various amino acids to each other. It is the 3-D shape of the protein that gives the protein its particular function. An analogy of the results of protein folding is the production of a paper boat from a flat sheet of paper. Although its source is a 2-D sheet of paper, by making a 3-D boat, the paper can perform work—that is, it can move along the surface of water and even carry cargo.

The rules for protein folding are still an interesting and active question in biological research. Some rules that are clear are that hydrophobic (water-hating) amino acids minimize their contact with the aqueous cytoplasm of the cell. These amino acids are often found in the interior of a protein. Hydrophilic (water-loving) amino acids will interact with the cytoplasm. They are usually found on the surface of a protein. Oppositely charged amino acids are attracted to each other.

A. Using the following information about the chemistry of some amino acids, transform your string of amino acids into its 3-D shape.

HYDROPHOBIC: Valine, Leucine, Isoleucine, Methionine, Phenylalanine

HYDROPHILIC: Arginine, Histidine, Lysine, Asparagine, Glutamine

POSITIVELY CHARGED: Lysine, Arginine, Histidine

NEGATIVELY CHARGED: Aspartic Acid, Glutamic Acid

Changes to the DNA sequence are called **mutations**. When DNA is altered, the mRNA that is produced from the DNA is also altered and changes to protein structure and function can result.

B. Replace one nucleotide on your mRNA and see what effect it has on the protein produced. List the altered nucleotide and amino acid sequences and describe whether the 3-D structure was altered.

C. Is it possible that a change to the DNA would have no effect on protein structure? Why or why not?
Yes, if a nucleotide change results in a codon that calls for the same amino acid or one with very similar chemistry.

D. The addition or subtraction of one or two nucleotides (or multiples thereof) to the DNA results in a **frame shift** mutation. How would this affect the mRNA that is transcribed from the mutated DNA?
Different amino acids would be coded for after the frame shift.

E. Frame shift mutations often result in the production of a stop codon where there was not one before. List an altered nucleotide and amino acid sequence that would result in an early stop codon.

(20 minutes of one week (set up); 15 minutes the following week (evaluating results))

Materials:
- *Per lab group: 2 nutrient agar plates, permanent marker, paper towels, pack of 2 sterile applicator sticks (cotton tipped)*
- *For class: 37˚C incubator, Serratia marcescens culture (available from Carolina Biological Supply)*

LAB EXERCISE 7.4

Investigating the Regulation of Gene Expression

Returning to our cookbook analogy, imagine the dish you would make if you mixed all of the ingredients called for in EVERY RECIPE—a not very tasty and possibly even illness-provoking meal. Somehow a cell controls which ingredients (genes) are expressed within it. These genes are also expressed in a specific and orderly sequence—just as the ingredients making up a cake are added in a particular sequence in order to produce a cake that mixes and rises correctly.

The cells in our bodies have many mechanisms for controlling gene expression, including internal signals, signals from other organs of the body, and environmental cues. In this exercise, you will investigate the environmental control of gene expression in bacteria. Work in lab groups assigned by your instructor for this exercise.

A. Obtain two plates of nutrient agar from your lab instructor. Using a permanent marker, label one "Room Temperature" and the other "37°." Label both plates with the names of your lab group members.

B. Your instructor will provide you with a culture of *Serratia marcescens*. You will transfer a small amount of the culture to each plate, following the instructions below:

1. Remove one sterile applicator from its pack—do not touch the cotton tip of the applicator or allow it to touch any other surface.

2. Lift one side of the lid of the *S. marcescens* culture just enough to insert the applicator stick. Gently touch the cotton tip to the surface of the plate and pick up a small amount of bacteria. You should be able to see a small red spot on the tip of the applicator. Be sure to close the culture dish after you remove the applicator to avoid contamination.

3. Making sure that the applicator stick does not touch any other surface, lift the lid of one of your labeled agar-filled plates just enough to insert the applicator. Lightly move the tip of the applicator across the surface of the agar in a zigzag motion. This will deposit a thin layer of bacterial cells, which will divide and become a visible culture over the next few days.

4. Place the applicator stick on a paper towel and dispose of it according to your instructor's guidelines.

5. Repeat steps 1–4 to inoculate the second plate.

C. Place the 37° plate lid side down in the incubator and the room temperature plate (also lid side down) where your instructor specifies.

D. After the plates have incubated and a bacterial lawn formed, fill in your observations about the color of the bacterial lawn grown in different temperatures in the following table.

The red color of one of the colonies is caused by the protein prodigiosin.

TABLE 7.3 **Bacterial Color Observations**

Growth Temperature	Color of Bacterial Lawn
Room Temperature	*Red*
37°C	*White*

E. Answer the following questions. Be prepared to share your answers with your instructor and classmates.

1. According to your understanding of gene expression, in which temperature conditions are prodigiosin-producing genes expressed in this bacteria?

At room temperature

2. How can you tell that prodigiosin-producing genes are turned off at higher temperatures?

The white color of the colony

Instructors: **Serratia marcescens** *is classified as Biosafety Level 1, meaning that it is not known to cause disease in healthy individuals, but appropriate precautions should be taken. Sterile applicators and plates should be autoclaved— or immersed in a 10% bleach solution for 24 hours—before disposal in the regular garbage. A bacterial lawn will form within 24–48 hours of plate inoculation. If lab periods are one week apart, place these plates in a refrigerator after the lawn has formed.*

3. Why might pigment production be temperature-sensitive in these bacteria?

Good question. All we can say is that it is possible that this pigment offers some advantage at room temperatures that is not needed at higher temperatures.

(25 Minutes)

Suggestions: Students should read or review the text book material on GMOs prior to class. A Web-based GMO resource can be found at http://www.ucsusa.org/food_and_environment /genetic_engineering/

If you would prefer that the whole class debate the issue, you could split the class into two groups (one for and one against) and let them first prepare their arguments and then debate as a class. Students in our labs enjoyed this discussion and extended it into the lecture classroom.

LAB EXERCISE 7.5

Labeling GMOs Debate

Genetic modification of food products can involve moving a gene normally found in one organism into another organism. Because of the universality of the Genetic Code, a gene transferred from one organism to another can often be used to build the same protein, regardless of its origin. Foods are genetically modified (GM) to increase their shelf life and to decrease damage from pests and weather.

Concerns about the potential negative environmental and health effects of producing and consuming GM crops have led some citizens to fight for legislation requiring that modified foods be labeled so consumers can make informed decisions about what foods they choose to eat. The manufacturers of GM crops argue that labeling foods is expensive and will be viewed by consumers as a warning, even in the absence of any proven risk. They believe that this will decrease sales and curtail further innovation.

A. Get together with the students at your lab table and discuss the following:

1. Do you believe that modified foods should be labeled? Summarize your group's discussion.

2. What potential risks do you think GMO consumption and production pose to humans, farm animals, and the environment? Summarize your group's discussion.

TOPIC 7
_____

POST-LABORATORY QUIZ

TRANSCRIPTION, TRANSLATION, AND GENETICALLY MODIFIED ORGANISMS

1. Using the DNA as a template to make RNA is called _____.
   transcription

2. The enzyme that uses DNA as a template for the synthesis of a complementary copy of RNA is called _____.
   RNA polymerase

3. Why is the RNA produced by transcription called messenger RNA?
   Because it carries the protein building instructional message from the DNA

4. Translation occurs on structures called _____.
   ribosomes

5. If the DNA from a given gene reads CCATTTGGG, the mRNA transcribed would be _____ and the protein produced would consist of the amino acids _____.
   GGUAAACCC; glycine, lysine, proline.

6. How does the nucleotide sequence of the coding strand of a DNA molecule differ from the mRNA produced?
   Uracils are in place of thymines; otherwise the sequence is the same.

7. The subunits of proteins are _____.
   amino acids

8. What might be the impact of changing the order of amino acids for a given protein?
The shape of the protein would likely change, and therefore its ability to do its job would be impacted also.

9. UUU codes for the amino acid phenylalanine in humans and bacteria. This is due to which property of the Genetic Code?
Universality

10. Name one environmental factor that plays a role in gene expression, in at least some organisms.
Heat (other answers possible)

TOPIC 8
The Theory of Evolution

Learning Objectives

1. Summarize the theory of common descent.
2. Learn how scientists test hypotheses about evolutionary relationships and perform such a test.
3. Define homology and give examples of homologous structures.
4. Use the classification of a number of organisms to create a phylogeny of these organisms.
5. Distinguish between homology and analogy and discuss the role of each in creating and complicating phylogenies.
6. Describe how cladistic analysis is a systematic technique for determining phylogenetic relationships.

A pre-laboratory quiz is available in Appendix A on page 211.

Pre-laboratory Reading

One of the hypotheses Charles Darwin put forth in his book, *On the Origin of Species,* was that all modern organisms derive from a single common ancestor, and that differences between organisms today resulted from evolutionary changes that occurred as species diverged from one another. This once revolutionary idea is referred to as the **theory of common descent**. According to the theory of common descent, all modern organisms can be arranged in a "family tree," or **phylogeny**, that describes their relationship to each other. The theory of common descent is now well accepted as the best explanation for the origins of modern species.

Biologists who study the evolutionary history of living organisms are called **systematists**. Much of what a systematist does is propose hypotheses of relationships among species based on their similarities and differences. One of the generalizations of the science of **systematics** is that organisms that share more features are more closely related than organisms that share fewer features. By this reasoning, systematists think that shared features might have been present in the common ancestor of the organisms. Shared features among species that occur as a result of the species' shared relationships are known as **homologies**. Phylogenies are created by systematists based on their investigation of the homologies among species.

Phylogenies derived by systematists represent hypotheses of evolutionary relationship. These hypotheses can be tested using characteristics of the organisms that were *not* used to make the initial hypothesis. This is a bit like coming up with a hypothesis about which foods taste sour and which taste sweet using the appearance of the food, and then testing your hypothesis by measuring the foods' sugar (sweet) and acid (sour) content with some chemical tests. In this case, we can find out if we did a good job of classifying foods by actually tasting them. Systematists cannot, for the most part, know for certain if their hypothesis reflects a true evolutionary relationship, because they cannot travel back in time to observe the actual evolutionary events. However, multiple lines of evidence, including comparisons of DNA sequences and investigations of the fossil record, can provide strong support for a phylogenetic hypothesis.

Testing hypotheses of evolutionary relationship is especially important because not all similarities among organisms are homologies. In other words, two organisms that appear similar might not have similar features because they have a common ancestor. Instead, similar environmental conditions experienced by two distantly related organisms might favor the evolution of similar structures or features. Shared characteristics that arise as a result of shared environmental conditions are known as **analogies**. For example, dolphins appear superficially similar to sharks, with their streamlined bodies, lack of body hair, and generally gray color. These similarities are analogous, however, and reflect their similar lifestyles as ocean predators. Dolphins are actually more closely related to other mammals, such as otters and humans, than they are to sharks and fish. Dolphins and other mammals are similar because dolphins breathe air (rather than have gills), produce hair, and provide milk for their infants. Distinguishing between homology and analogy is one of the most difficult tasks a systematist faces.

Cladistic analysis, also known as **cladistics**, is a standardized technique for creating phylogenies. Cladistics allows a systematic comparison between the group of species whose relationship we want to determine (called the **ingroup**) and a species or group of species that is related to this group, but not a part of it (called the **outgroup**). For instance, if we were interested in the possible relationship among frog species, we might choose a toad species as the outgroup. In cladistic analysis, the only useful characters for constructing a phylogeny are those that are found in the ingroup, but not in the outgroup.

(15 Minutes)

LAB EXERCISE 8.1

Understanding Tree Diagrams

Phylogenies are often presented graphically in the form of a tree diagram (see Figure 8.1). On these **phylogenetic trees**, all of the modern organisms we are interested in understanding the relationship among are found at the tips of the branches. The junctions between branches lower down on the tree represent common ancestors to these modern organisms. Junctions near the top of the tree represent more recent common ancestry than junctions near the base of the tree.

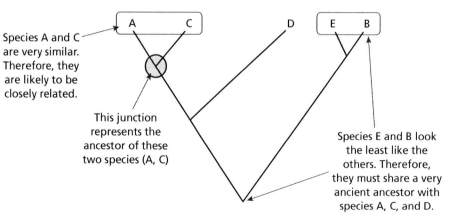

Species A and C are very similar. Therefore, they are likely to be closely related.

This junction represents the ancestor of these two species (A, C)

Species E and B look the least like the others. Therefore, they must share a very ancient ancestor with species A, C, and D.

FIGURE 8.1

A. Draw your family's phylogenetic tree.

It can be helpful to understanding a phylogenetic tree to relate it to relationships that you already know about.

1. Fill in the following table, as best you can.

TABLE 8.1

Relationship to You	Name of Person
A. Self	
B. Full Sibling (Brother or Sister)	
C. First Cousin	
D. Parent (from your first cousin's side of the family)	
E. Grandparent (Father or mother of the parent you have listed)	

2. Using the information from Table 8.1, fill in the following tree:

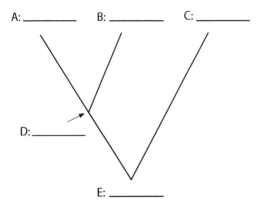

A: _____   B: _____   C: _____

D: _____

E: _____

FIGURE 8.2

B. Answer the following questions:

1. Who is the common ancestor of all of the individuals on the tree?
   Grandparent

2. Why does the diagram place only you, your sibling, and your cousin at the branch tips?

These individuals represent the current generation, whereas your parent and grandparent represent "ancestral" generations.

3. How is this tree different than those produced by biologists attempting to determine the evolutionary relationship among species?

Several ways: these are relationships among individuals, not different species. Some of the "ancestral" individuals on the tree above may still be living, whereas in an actual phylogenetic tree, the ancestors are most likely extinct. Most importantly, with actual phylogenetic trees, we do not know the real relationship among individual species, but are attempting to uncover those relationships by systematic observation.

(20 Minutes)

Materials:
The information in the instructor's manual relies on the following mammal skulls: cat, dog, mink, muskrat, sheep, and pig. These skulls are available from the company Science Kit and Boreal Laboratories for a total price of approximately $450 for all six. Ideally, a lab of 24 students should have three to six sets available. Skulls or specimens should be labeled A–F.

However, the instructions in the actual lab are general and do not refer to actual species, allowing you to use any skeletal materials you might have on hand. Of course, if you do not use the materials listed here, you will have to do additional research about classification and DNA sequences to provide to the students during the other parts of the laboratory.

Instructors: The following tables provide sample data. This is not necessarily the "correct" answer, but it is included to give you some guidance about how this exercise can work.

LAB EXERCISE 8.2

Examine Homologies Among Skulls or Skeletons

In the next several lab exercises, you will create a phylogeny of organisms using many of the same techniques employed by professional systematists. Except when they are working with organismal groups with good fossil records, systematists are limited to information gleaned from living organisms when discerning phylogenetic relationships. The first step is often careful observation of the shared characteristics found within the group of organisms they are studying.

A. Observe the skulls and/or skeletons of the vertebrate species available. Look for features that some or all of the different specimens have in common. For example, look at the placement of the eyes, the shape of the nose, the type of teeth and their number and distribution in the mouth, and the structure of the bones around the eye socket (Figure 8.3). For now, we will assume that all similarities are homologies.

B. Record your observations in Table 8.2, by listing one character (for example, "presence of large canine teeth") in each row and then placing a " + " or a " − " in each corresponding column, indicating the presence or absence of the character.

TABLE 8.2

Character	Species A	Species B	Species C	Species D	Species E	Species F
Enlarged canines	+	+	−	+	−	+
Eyes face forward	+	+		+	−	−
Large yellowish incisors	−	−	+	−	−	−
Grinding molars	−	−	+	−	+	+
Long snout	−	+	−	−	+	+
Eye orbit completely encircled by bone	−	−	+	−	+	−

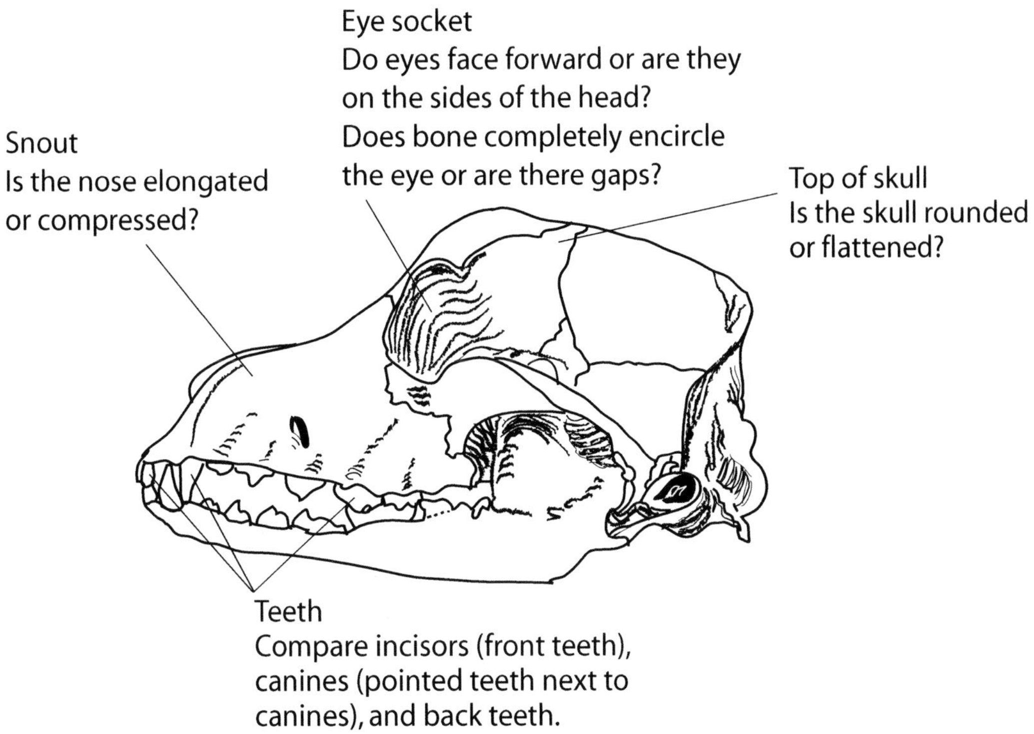

Snout
Is the nose elongated
or compressed?

Eye socket
Do eyes face forward or are they
on the sides of the head?
Does bone completely encircle
the eye or are there gaps?

Top of skull
Is the skull rounded
or flattened?

Teeth
Compare incisors (front teeth),
canines (pointed teeth next to
canines), and back teeth.

FIGURE 8.3

C. For each pair of species, count the number of shared " + " or " − " marks (i.e. where the symbol for the character for both species is identical). These shared characters are assumed to be homologies. How many presumed homologies does each animal share with each other animal (Fill in Table 8.3)?

The most important goal of this exercise is to have the students observe the specimens closely and to spend time looking for similarities and differences. Allow students the freedom to define the characteristics themselves and determine what degree of similarity among specimens can be called "homology." Emphasize that the point is not for them to come up with the same hypothesis as the "experts," but to use their observation skills and creativity to develop their own hypothesis of relationship (Exercise 8.3).

TABLE 8.3

A + B	5	B + C	0	C + D	1	D + E	1
A + C	1	B + D	5	C + E	4	D + F	3
A + D	6	B + E	2	C + F	2		
A + E	1	B + F	4			E + F	4
A + F	3						

LAB EXERCISE 8.3

Generate a Hypothesis of Evolutionary Relationship Among Species Based on Homology

(15 Minutes)

A. Draw a phylogenetic tree.

Remember that one of the generalizations of the science of systematics is that organisms that share more features are more closely related than organisms that share fewer features, and that these shared features were

Instructors: Students will struggle with this part of the assignment. Take the time to walk them through an example of how to group species into larger and larger "units" so that they can see how it works. They can do it, but they need to understand that it takes some mental gymnastics.

present in the common ancestor of the organisms. Given this generalization, use the data generated in the second table in Lab Exercise 8.2 to develop a preliminary hypothesis of evolutionary relationship among these animals.

To create the tree, we use the basic principle that species that have a recent common ancestor have many traits in common, whereas species that have a more distant common ancestor have fewer traits in common. After you have grouped species into pairs by the number of shared characteristics as in Table 8.3, look for pairs of species that have the greatest number of similarities—you can assume that these are the closest relatives.

Combine the pairs you have made into larger groups by looking at the number of characteristics each pair shares with another species or pair of species. To determine this, you should have to go back to Table 8.2, examine the characteristics that each pair of species shares, and see how many of these *common* characteristics are shared with other species. Note that it is very likely that you will need to make judgment calls about relationships among some of the species. For example, species A and C might share three homologies, A and B might share three homologies, but B and C might only share two. To resolve the relationship among these three species, you will have to decide which similarities are more likely to be true homologies and which may be analogies. Continue this process until all species are united into a single tree, representing a hierarchy of similarities.

Draw your proposed phylogenetic tree in the space here. At each branch point on the tree, indicate the homologies that presumably were present in the common ancestor of a group of species. Be prepared to share your analysis with your instructor and classmates.

Students often have difficulty drawing a phylogenetic tree. Many will want to draw a tree where one modern species appears to be "ancestral" to other modern species. You might want to review Figure 8.1 (from Lab Exercise 8.1) with students to help them visualize what they are attempting to create. You should also circulate among students as they are engaged in drawing the tree to check for any misunderstandings.

Based on the sample data provided earlier, the tree might look as follows (some "judgment calls" had to be made).

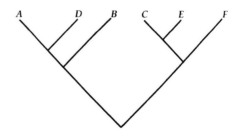

B. Answer the following questions and be prepared to share your answers with your instructor and classmates.

1. Compare your phylogenetic tree with those created by your classmates. Are there any universal similarities? What is the origin of any key differences?

   There are two major sources of difference. One is a difference in the characters used in their analysis and their assignment of organisms to "presence/absence" categories for the character. The other is a difference among the groups in their decisions about which shared characteristics are homologous and which are analogous. These differences among trees can lead to a lively discussion about how an "expert" might solve these problems (also see the following question 2).

2. Systematists who specialize in studying the evolutionary relationship among vertebrates use their knowledge of the group to choose characters for phylogenetic analysis and to make assumptions about which shared traits are likely to be homologies and which are likely to be analogies. In

general, traits that are highly subject to change via natural selection (for example, coat color in mammals) are less likely to be homologous among species than traits that are less subject to change (for example, cold-bloodedness). What types of characters in this group might be more useful to creating phylogenies? Why do you think so? What evidence would support the hypothesis that a particular trait contains more information about evolutionary relationship than another trait?

This question is a significant challenge for most students. Encourage them to think about how "difficult" a particular evolutionary change might be from a genetic standpoint; for instance, a change in overall size can probably result from a change in a single gene controlling time of development, but a change in dentition and thus diet would probably require changes in genes that determine tooth anatomy as well as changes in physiology genes (to accommodate the new diet). Thus similarity in size might be more likely to be analogy, while similarity in dentition might be more likely to be homology.

3. The different trees generated by different students in the lab represent alternative hypotheses about the evolutionary relationships among this group of organisms. What additional information would allow you to test these hypotheses and determine which ones are more likely to reflect the true phylogeny?

Additional information about physiology, development, nonskeletal anatomy, protein and DNA sequence comparisons, the fossil record, biogeography, and behavior.

LAB EXERCISE 8.4

(15 Minutes)

Test a Hypothesis of Evolutionary Relationship by Examining the Classification of the Species in Your Analysis

A. Review the classification system.

In the eighteenth century, the Swedish botanist Carolus Linnaeus created the modern biological classification system. Within this system, each species is placed within a hierarchy that groups organisms according to ever broader similarities. The hierarchy takes the following basic form:

Kingdom (broadest classification)
Phylum
Class
Order
Family
Genus
Species (narrowest classification)

Each of these categories is generally called a **taxonomic rank**.

Linnaeus' classification system has become the standard method of organizing biological diversity. Since his time, systematists have found it necessary to add "sub" and "super" ranks to help group organisms more finely; for instance, subfamily is a taxonomic rank that falls between family and genus.

Modern classification of species generally uses similarities and differences among modern organisms to determine their places in the hierarchy. Species that share a large number of specific similarities are placed in a narrower taxonomic rank together, while species that share fewer specific

Materials: Classification information to provide to students is located in Appendix B, p. 235. To complete this part of the exercise, you will have to identify for students which species is skull A, which is skull B, and so on. With the classification information in the appendix, students have enough information to draw an unambiguous tree diagram. However, you might choose to omit the superorder classification and thus leave room for discussion of the difficulty in determining relationships among the three orders represented here when using just the traditional classification system.

similarities, but some broad similarities, are placed in broader taxonomic groups. Note that this is similar to how we grouped organisms using homology in the previous lab exercise. The implication of grouping organisms this way is also similar—organisms in narrower taxonomic groups are presumed to share a more recent common ancestor than organisms in broader taxonomic groups. Therefore, we assume that two species in the same genus share a recent common ancestor, while two groups of genera in the same family share a common ancestor that is slightly less recent.

B. Use the classification of your study organisms to create a hypothesis of evolutionary relationship.

Your lab instructor will distribute the Linnaean classification of each of the organisms you have observed. Use this information and your review of part A of this lab exercise to generate a phylogeny that reflects the evolutionary relationship among these organisms implied by their classification. Draw your phylogenetic tree in this space, and be prepared to share it with your lab instructor and classmates.

Here is the "real" tree (letters are from the key in Exercise 8.2):

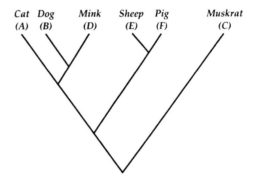

Cat	Dog	Mink	Sheep	Pig	Muskrat
(A)	(B)	(D)	(E)	(F)	(C)

C. Answer the following questions:

1. Compare your phylogenetic tree with those drawn by other students in the class. How are they similar? How are they different? What is the origin of these differences?

2. Compare the phylogenetic tree you have created here with the tree you drew in Lab Exercise 8.2. How are they similar? How are they different?

3. The phylogenetic trees you drew for Lab Exercises 8.3 and 8.4, if they are different, now represent alternative hypotheses for the evolutionary relationships among these species. What other information could you use to test which of these hypotheses is more likely to represent the evolutionary relationship? (Note: even if your trees were identical, additional information would help support the hypothesis they represent.)

DNA or protein sequence analysis, the fossil record, biogeography, behavior.

LAB EXERCISE 8.5

Test Your Hypothesis of Evolutionary Relationship by Comparing DNA Sequences Using Cladistic Analysis

A. Analyze DNA sequence data.

The spreadsheet your instructor has distributed describes a segment of the DNA sequence for a gene that is common to all of the species in this analysis. Although this gene performs a similar function in every animal, slight differences in its DNA sequence among various organisms can provide clues about the possible relationship of these organisms to each other.

On the spreadsheet, a number at the top of each column indicates the position of each nucleotide in the gene sequence. You should notice that all species are identical at many of the positions—for a cladistic analysis, we are only interested in positions where there is a difference in nucleotides among animals. Examine the spreadsheet closely and find the positions where nucleotides are different among members of the ingroup. In Table 8.4, indicate the position number and the nucleotide for each species, including the outgroup, at that position.

B. A phylogenetic tree based on cladistic analysis of DNA data.

Recall that cladistics analyzes the relationship among organisms in the ingroup by looking at how members of the group differ from the outgroup. To determine this, you must summarize the information you have collected by indicating the number of **shared differences from the outgroup** for each species pair in the analysis.

(25 Minutes)

Materials:
- *DNA sequences – See Appendix B, page 236, for a DNA sequence handout. This DNA sequence data is based on work described in Murphy, W.J. et al.,* **Nature 409: 614–618** *(although some changes were made to remove ambiguity from the analysis—in the interest of full disclosure, if you use this data, you should probably tell the students that it is* <u>slightly</u> *fudged). The gene sequenced for this analysis is known as ADORA3, which codes for a protein found in certain cell membranes that acts as a receptor for adenosine. The outgroup on this data sheet is the opossum, a marsupial mammal (all others in analysis are placental).*
- *Colored highlighters—one for each student group*

Instructors: Again, students are challenged by the complexity of this exercise. In our experience, nonmajors can handle this, but again need help understanding the mental gymnastics involved.

TABLE 8.4

DNA Sequence Position	Outgroup	Species A	Species B	Species C	Species D	Species E	Species F
30	C	C	C	C	C	T	T
41	T	A	A	T	A	A	A
42	T	C	C	C	C	C	C
48	C	C	C	C	C	T	C
51	T	C	C	T	C	T	T
54	C	C	C	G	C	C	C
57	A	C	C	C	C	T	T
63	C	T	T	C	T	T	T
64	C	T	T	T	T	C	C
66	C	A	A	C	A	C	C
69	C	C	C	C	C	T	T
72	T	C	C	T	C	C	C
73	T	C	C	C	C	C	C
75	G	G	A	G	A	G	G
76	G	G	G	C	A	G	G

Begin by reading down each ingroup column and highlighting cells where the DNA base in that column is different from the base in the corresponding cell in the outgroup column. When you have completed this for each column, compare ingroup columns to each other. When cells in the same row in both columns are highlighted, check the bases in each to make sure that they are identical to each other; if they are, this represents a <u>shared difference</u> from the outgroup. If they are both different from the outgroup but also different from each other, this is not a shared difference. Record the number of shared differences for each species pair in Table 8.5.

TABLE 8.5

A and B	9	B and C	4	C and D	4	D and E	5
A and C	4	B and D	10	C and E	2	D and F	5
A and D	9	B and E	5	C and F	2		
A and E	5	B and F	5			E and F	8
A and F	5						

Use the information from Table 8.5 to draw a new phylogenetic tree, grouping species by the number of shared derived characteristics. As with your first phylogenetic tree, group pairs of species into larger groups by determining the number of shared differences each pair shares with a different pair. Draw the tree here and be prepared to share it with your lab instructor and classmates.

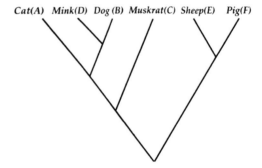

C. Discuss the following questions and be prepared to share your answers with your lab instructor and classmates:

1. How does this tree compare to your first two trees? Did analysis of DNA data support your initial hypothesis? In what ways did it not?

2. Compare the trees produced by different groups using the DNA data. Do all groups agree on the relationship among these species? Why is this?

   All trees should be very close, if not identical, because the cladistic method is repeatable and does not (typically) require scientists to make judgment calls.

3. What other sets of data could you use to test and refine your hypothesis of relationship among these mammals?

DNA sequences of other genes, protein sequences, the fossil record, biogeography, behavior.

LAB EXERCISE 8.6

(20 Minutes)

Wrap-up Discussion

The exercises in this laboratory are directed toward the task of creating and testing a hypothesis of evolutionary relationship among relatively closely related species. However, we can extend these ideas to less obviously similar groups of organisms and think about the data that would allow us to test the hypothesis that organisms as diverse as humans and mushrooms, and indeed all living species, share a common ancestor. Answer the following questions and be prepared to discuss them with your lab instructor and classmates.

A. What basic similarities among mammals and differences between mammals (the ingroup) and reptiles (an outgroup) help support the hypothesis that all mammals share a common ancestor? What additional evidence would help you test this hypothesis?

All mammals have hair at some stage of life, most give birth to live young (with the exception of monotremes), all provide young with milk. Reptiles have scales, their young hatch from eggs, and do not provide young with milk.

The hypothesis could also be tested via DNA sequence analysis and examination of the fossil record.

B. What similarities between mammals and fungi exist? Do these similarities indicate that they both arose from a common ancestor? How could you test your hypothesis?

Both mammals and fungi are eukaryotic and heterotrophic. Cell structure is largely the same, as well as the basics of cellular physiology.

You could test this hypothesis via analysis of DNA sequence data.

C. What similarities do all living organisms, from bacteria to dragonflies, share? Are these similarities convincing evidence supporting the theory of evolution? Explain your answer.

All organisms have DNA, same basic process of transcription and translation, same genetic code.

TOPIC 8 _____

POST-LABORATORY QUIZ

THE THEORY OF EVOLUTION

1. Describe the theory of common descent.

   All organisms present on Earth today arose from a single common ancestor in the distant past.

2. Define "homology."

   A trait found in two different species that was found in their common ancestor. In other words, a homologous trait is one that is similar by descent.

3. Examine the following phylogenetic tree. Which two organisms probably have the greatest number of homologies? Which two are the descendants of the most recent common ancestor?

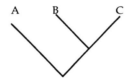

   B and C for both questions

4. Put these taxonomic groups in order from most inclusive to least inclusive.

   Order, Genus, Family, Species, Phylum

   Phylum, Order, Family, Genus, Species

5. Draw the relationship among these three organisms that is implied by their classification:

   1. Asparagus. Order Liliales, Family Liliaceae, *Asparagus officinalis*
   2. Yam. Order Liliales, Family Discoreacea, *Discorea species*
   3. Daffodil. Order Liliales, Family Liliaceae, *Narcissus pseudonarcissus*

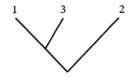

6. How can a hypothesized phylogeny that is implied by the Linnaean classification of a group of related species be tested?

Comparisons of DNA sequence, amino acid sequence in proteins, analysis of the fossil record.

7. What is the function of the outgroup in a cladistic analysis?

The characteristics of the outgroup provide a basis for determining which traits found in the ingroup represent "newly evolved" features.

8. Butterflies have wings and bats have wings. Is this similarity a homology or analogy? Explain your answer.

It is an analogy, because the common ancestor of butterflies (an insect) and bats (a mammal) very likely did not have wings. This is most likely the case because few mammals have wings. Additionally, the wings of a butterfly and the wings of a bat are different structurally.

9. Describe two characteristics shared by all living organisms, and which are probably homologous among all organisms.

DNA as genetic material, identical genetic code (relationship between DNA codons and amino acids), and so on.

10. What factors cause some organisms to look superficially similar despite the lack of a close ancestral relationship among them? As part of your answer, give an example of two organisms with analogous traits.

When two organisms face similar environmental challenges, natural selection might favor similar adaptations in both organisms. An example of this is the similarity in overall shape between sharks and dolphins—both are oceanic predators and have streamlined shapes to help them move through the water rapidly—despite the fact that dolphins are more closely related to hippos and horses than to sharks.

TOPIC 9

Natural Selection

Learning Objectives

1. Describe the theory of natural selection.
2. Define the terms "fitness" and "adaptation" in the context of the theory of natural selection.
3. Demonstrate how similar populations can become different as a result of natural selection in different environments.
4. Demonstrate how competition for resources might lead to evolution.
5. Use an understanding of the theory of natural selection to explain how a unique feature of a species might have evolved.
6. Relate the origins of variants in a population to the process of mutation.
7. Relate the change in the frequency of an adaptation in a population to a change in the frequency of certain alleles in that population.

A pre-laboratory quiz is available in Appendix A on page 213.

Pre-laboratory Reading

Evolution refers to the changes that occur in the characteristics of populations over the course of generations. One of the causes of evolution is the process of **natural selection**. According to the theory of natural selection, the natural variation among individuals within a population of organisms results in differences among them in their ability to survive and/or reproduce in a given environment. Traits that increase the chance of survival and/or reproduction are called **adaptations**. Individuals with adaptations are defined as having greater **fitness** than other individuals in the population—meaning that they have more surviving offspring. Many of these offspring carry their parents' adaptations, leading to these adaptations becoming more common in a population and other nonadaptive traits becoming less common. In other words, natural selection results in a change in the characteristics of the population— the population evolves.

Traits that become common in a population are limited by the variation that is present in the population and are a function of the environment that the population inhabits. Predators are an environmental factor that causes natural selection—traits that allow individuals to better avoid death through **predation** should spread in a population of prey species. However, many of the traits that are favored by natural selection are subtler in their effect. These are adaptations that improve fitness by making their possessors better **competitors** for a limited resource in the environment. Individuals without such adaptations might not be more likely to die as a result, but they will have fewer successful offspring.

For an adaptation to become common in a population through the process of natural selection, the trait must have a genetic basis. That is, individuals who possess the adaptation must carry a different allele, or set of alleles, compared to those who do not possess the adaptation. The increased fitness of individuals with a particular adaptation means that they produce a large number of surviving offspring who carry the adaptive allele. We can now understand that evolution via the process of natural selection results in a change in the frequency of a particular allele in a population—adaptive alleles become more common and nonadaptive ones become less common.

Understanding the relationship between genes and adaptations also helps us to see how new adaptations arise—through changes in genes, or **mutation**. Mutation is a random process that can have a variety of results—from negative, to neutral, to beneficial. Only a few mutations result in adaptations. In addition, a mutation that results in an adaptation in a particular environment can be neutral, or even harmful, in another environment.

(30 Minutes)

LAB EXERCISE 9.1

Model the Process of Natural Selection Resulting from Predation

A. Simulate the process of natural selection by acting as a "selector," in this case a predator.

The containers of shredded paper available at your lab table represent the habitat (living space) of the prey population. The prey will be represented by pipe cleaners (for prey, they are pretty slow, but they *can* hide.)

1. Work in pairs for this exercise. First, decide which member of the pair will act as the "predator" in this habitat and which will be the "prey handler."
2. The predator should turn away while the prey handler hides eight of each color of pipe cleaner within the habitat. Prey do not have to rest on the surface of the paper, but can be buried within the habitat.
3. The predator will now hunt and capture as many prey as possible during a single generation time—in this simulation, 20 seconds. To capture the prey, the predators should use keen eyesight, but also can use their hands to "search" around the habitat—that is, to move paper. When a pipe cleaner is located, it should be placed in the prey container provided.
4. When the time is up, count the number of prey in the container (if a prey was picked up but dropped, it should not be counted—klutzy predators don't eat).
5. Fill in Table 9.1 and add the appropriate number of new prey to the habitat to make the next generation.

Primary color of habitat   *brown*

Instructors:
If you plan on doing both Lab Exercises 9.1 and 9.2, we suggest splitting larger labs (20–24 students) into two groups, and then having subgroups of one half work on Exercise 9.1 and subgroups of the other half work on Exercise 9.2 at the same time. Follow this by switching when all the groups have completed the exercise (that is, three groups of four students work on Exercise 9.1, while three groups of four students work on Exercise 9.2—this cuts the preparation needs in half). We have found that both exercises as written take about the same time. If groups differ in the time it takes them to complete the task, you can assign a scenario from Exercise 9.3 to idle groups.

Materials:
- *Pipe cleaners, cut into 5-cm sections; 150 sections of each of 3 different (distinct) colors.*
- *Shredded paper habitats—three different basic colors, 1 habitat per 2 students.*
- *Large plastic bin to hold paper, about 18″ × 24″ × 6″ deep.*
- *Shredded paper, enough to fill bin about 3 inches deep. You can shred colored office paper into confetti-sized bits using most standard office shredders. Each of the three different "habitats" should have a primary color, but should also contain some of the other habitat colors as well as white—a mixture is more effective camouflage. Each of the habitats should hide at least one of the pipe cleaner colors (but not all three) well.*
- *Containers for pipe cleaners (paper cups, small beakers), 3 per student group.*
- *Containers for captured prey items (petri dish, watch glass), 1 per student group.*
- *See Appendix B, page 237, for a table to record student results. The number of rows depends on the number of student groups.*

Instructors: Sample data provided for your information.

TABLE 9.1

	Prey Type 1	Prey Type 2	Prey Type 3
	brown	*green*	*red*
A. Number in habitat at start	8	8	8
B. Number in prey container after hunt	*1*	*4*	*7*
C. Number remaining in habitat after hunt (= A − B)	*7*	*4*	*1*
D. New offspring (each survivor has one offspring = C) Add these prey to the habitat.	*7*	*4*	*1*
E. Total number in habitat at beginning of next generation (= C + D)	*14*	*8*	*2*

6. Perform a hunt of this "second generation" with the same predator and prey handler, record the results in Table 9.2, and add the appropriate number of new prey to the habitat.

TABLE 9.2

	Prey Type 1 _____	Prey Type 2 _____	Prey Type 3 _____
F. Number in habitat at start (= E from previous table)			
G. Number in prey container after hunt			
H. Number remaining in habitat after hunt (= F − G)			
I. New offspring (each survivor has one offspring = H) Add these to the habitat.			
J. Total number in habitat at beginning of next generation (= H + I)			

7. Perform a hunt of the third generation with the same predator and prey handler and record the results in Table 9.3.

TABLE 9.3

	Prey Type 1 _____	Prey Type 2 _____	Prey Type 3 _____
K. Number in habitat at start (= J from previous table)			
L. Number in prey container after hunt			
M. Number remaining in habitat after hunt (= K − L)			
N. New offspring (each survivor has one offspring = M)			
O. Total number in habitat at beginning of next generation (= M + N)			

8. Remove all prey from the habitat when you are done and post your results on the table provided by your lab instructor.
9. If time allows, switch positions with another pair of students who are using a different habitat type and repeat the three rounds of the simulation (use Tables 9.4, 9.5, 9.6). The predator and prey handler can switch "jobs" for this simulation.

Primary habitat color: _____

TABLE 9.4 **Simulation Round 1**

	Prey Type 1 _____	Prey Type 2 _____	Prey Type 3 _____
A. Number in habitat at start	8	8	8
B. Number in prey container after hunt			
C. Number remaining in habitat after hunt (= A − B)			
D. New offspring (each survivor has one offspring = C) Add these to the habitat.			
E. Total number in habitat at beginning of next generation (= C + D)			

TABLE 9.5 **Simulation Round 2**

	Prey Type 1 _____	Prey Type 2 _____	Prey Type 3 _____
F. Number in habitat at start (= E from previous table)			
G. Number in prey container after hunt			
H. Number remaining in habitat after hunt (= F − G)			
I. New offspring (each survivor has one offspring = H) Add these to the habitat.			
J. Total number in habitat at beginning of next generation (= H + I)			

TABLE 9.6 **Simulation Round 3**

	Prey Type 1 _____	Prey Type 2 _____	Prey Type 3 _____
K. Number in habitat at start (= J from previous table)			
L. Number in prey container after hunt			
M. Number remaining in habitat after hunt (= K − L)			
N. New offspring (each survivor has one offspring = M)			
O. Total number in habitat at beginning of next generation (= M + N)			

10. Remove all prey from the habitat when you are done and post your results on the table provided by your lab instructor.

B. Discuss the following questions and be prepared to share your answers with your lab instructor and classmates:

1. Compare the population of pipe cleaners at the end of the first simulation to the population of pipe cleaners at the beginning of the simulation. Did the population evolve in response to natural selection by the predator?
   Yes

2. Compare the population of pipe cleaners at the end of the first simulation to the population of pipe cleaners at the beginning of the simulation. Did the population evolve differently in different habitats? Why?
   The population did evolve differently in different habitats. This is because in each different colored habitat, a different prey color is favored by natural selection, i.e., it is more difficult for the predator to find.

3. Can you think of prey species in nature that have adaptations that reduce their risk of death by predation? Describe some examples.
   Organisms that use speed to escape predators (for example, impalas). Organisms that use camouflage to avoid notice by predators (for example, moths with tree bark-like wing patterns). Organisms that have structures that "discourage" predation (for example, porcupine quills). Organisms that attempt to scare off predators (for example, caterpillars with "snake head" back ends). Organisms with chemical defenses (for example, skunks, monarch butterflies).

4. How would you expect your results (or those of your classmates) to differ if all of the individuals of one of the easy-to-find prey types produced three offspring upon surviving predation? Can you think of prey species in nature that are easy to catch but have high rates of reproduction? Give an example.
   This easy-to-find type would still have high fitness relative to hard-to-find types because it is so rapidly reproducing. It should remain common in the population. Many insects and small mammals might fit this category.

LAB EXERCISE 9.2

Model the Effects of Mutation and Competition on Evolution by Natural Selection

A. Simulate competition for food among wading birds.

1. Work in teams of four to complete this exercise. Add to your team's aquarium four of each type of food for each person in your group. Each student should then select an "average length" bird bill (one set of short chopsticks). Practice using these to pick up the "food items" *with one hand* until you feel comfortable with how the bill works.

2. Everyone will feed together for a round of 30 seconds, according to the following rules:
   - Food must be picked up by your bill. Do not use the edge of the container to roll the food out of the basin.
   - Pick up only one piece of food at a time.
   - No portion of your hand may enter the water while you are fishing. If it does, you must forfeit the food item.

3. At the end of the round, record the number of pieces of food of each type picked up by each student on Table 9.7.

(20 Minutes)

Materials:
- *10-gallon aquaria, 1 per 4 students. (See instructions before Exercise 9.1 about splitting the lab into two groups). Aquaria should be filled with water so that a student using the "short" chopsticks to pick up a food item lying on the bottom of the aquarium would have to get his hand wet to do so, but that those using longer chopsticks will stay dry.*
- *Soft plastic fish- or grub-shaped fishing lures, 50 per student group: 25 with sinkers and 25 identical or nearly so, without sinkers. You should be able to find lures of this type at any large outdoors store for less than $5 per 25 lures. If not available in your area, try the Cabela's web site at www.cabelas.com and search for "soft plastic fishing lures."*
- *Chopsticks—8 sets per student group. 4 sets should be cut to 1/2 length—these are the "average length bills."*
- *Dice—1 pair per student group.*

Instructors: Five rounds might seem like too many, but because they last only 30 seconds, they pass quickly. We have never had students complain about the repetition; they enjoy the "competitive" aspect too much.

TABLE 9.7   **Round 1**

Bird Name	Total Number of Food Items

4. To symbolize the production of the next generation, each student should roll two dice.

    If you roll any number besides 7, your offspring will have the same bill type as you. If you roll a 7, your offspring will carry a mutation for bill length. Now roll a *single* die to determine the nature of the mutation, as follows:

    • If you roll a 1 or 2, the mutation results in no change in bill length.
    • If you roll a 3, 4, 5, or 6, the mutation results in a longer bill. Pick up a longer bill and practice with it a few times before the next round.

5. Do another feeding round following the preceding rules and record the results in Tables 9.8 – 9.11. Repeat the protocol for determining the traits of the next generation. You should complete five rounds of feeding in total.

TABLE 9.8   **Round 2**

Bird	Beak Length	Total Number of Food Items

TABLE 9.9   **Round 3**

Bird	Beak Length	Total Number of Food Items

TABLE 9.10   **Round 4**

Bird	Beak Length	Total Number of Food Items

TABLE 9.11   **Round 5**

Bird	Beak Length	Total Number of Food Items

B. Answer the following discussion questions and be prepared to share your answers with your instructor and classmates.

1. What is the significance of using a roll of the dice to determine whether mutation occurs? How does this compare to how mutations actually occur?

   A dice roll introduces randomness into the simulation—mutations are random occurrences.

2. The chance of getting a 7 when rolling two dice is 1 in 6. How do you think this compares to the chance of mutation occurring in any one gene?

   Much more likely than an actual mutation

3. When a mutation occurs in a "family" (in this simulation, one person represents a "family" of birds), does that change the likelihood that another mutation will occur in that family? Explain.

   No, because mutation is random, a mutation has an equal chance of occurring anywhere in any generation.

4. What is the significance of the second roll of the dice (that is, after someone determines that a mutation has occurred)? How does this second roll correspond to the effect of a mutation in nature?

   A mutation can be harmful, neutral, or beneficial. In this simulation, there is no "harmful" outcome and the beneficial outcome is probably much more likely than it would be in nature.

5. Did bill length have an influence on feeding success? How?

6. How might the amount of food an individual consumes affect that individual's reproductive success (that is, number of offspring)? Describe specifically how more food benefits females and how it benefits males.

   More food for female wading birds might mean that they can produce more eggs or healthier eggs. More food for males might mean that they are stronger and better able to compete with other males for females or are more attractive to females who are choosing mates.

7. This simulation did not allow for changes in the population due to differences in reproductive success. Given the differences among individuals in bill length and in feeding success, how do you think the population you modeled might have evolved?

   If longer bills increase feeding success in this environment and if increased feeding success leads to greater reproductive success, then we would expect the frequency of long bills to increase in the population over time.

8. In the lab introduction, evolution was defined as a change in allele frequency in a population over the course of generations. Did the frequency of the "long bill" allele change in your population of birds (that is, within your laboratory group) over the five generations modeled here? Was this change a result of natural selection? Why not?

   Typically the frequency will change (at least one student will "gain" the long bill trait), but this is not a result of natural selection because the simulation does not allow the birds to differ in reproductive success. The frequency changed solely as a result of mutation.

9. Does this simulation illustrate how a new species might evolve from an ancestral species? In what way?

   Mutation introduces novel variations into a population. If one of these variations is adaptive, it will become common in the population. If the variation is different enough, or if the population is isolated from other populations of the same species, we could classify the changed population as a new species.

10. Comment on how this simulation is a good model of what happens in nature and how it is a poor model of natural processes.

    It is a good model because it incorporates the randomness of mutation and illustrates the principle of adaptation. However, it is a poor model because the possession of an adaptation does not translate into reproductive success, as it does in nature.

(25 Minutes)

Instructors: Note that, generally, these scenarios are arranged from simplest (1) to most complex (6). If you are using these to help smooth out time differences among student groups, you might want to assign number 6 to the fastest group, 5 to the second fastest, and so on. See Appendix B, page 238 for scenarios.

LAB EXERCISE 9.3

Practice Applying Your Understanding of Natural Selection

Each group of students will receive a description of an adaptation in a particular species from the lab instructor. Your task is to discuss this adaptation with your group and describe a reasonable scenario of how it might have evolved in the species. You will present this to the rest of the class. Your presentation should include the following points:

- What were the features of this species before the adaptation arose?
- How did the adaptation likely arise?
- What was the fitness advantage to individuals who possessed this adaptation relative to others who lacked it?
- What are the disadvantages of this adaptation? How might its advantages/disadvantages lead to different outcomes in different environments?

TOPIC 9

POST-LABORATORY QUIZ

NATURAL SELECTION

1. How does natural selection cause evolution?

    Natural selection is the differential survival and reproduction of individuals within a population. Individuals with certain traits, called adaptations, have greater survival and reproductive success (that is, fitness) than those without these traits. These traits have a genetic basis; thus there will be more individuals in the next generation with the adaptation. Over the course of several generations, the trait will become common—evolution has occurred in the population.

2. Why don't all populations of a species have the same adaptations? (Hint: Think about the exercise where you used pipe cleaners as prey animals.)

    Two reasons: 1) Not all populations may have individuals that have the appropriate mutation (that is, an adaptation may not arise in some populations); 2) Not all populations experience the same environments; a trait that is adaptive in one environment may be harmful in another.

3. Consider the data in Table 9.12.

TABLE 9.12   Pipe Cleaner Colors

Generation	Green	Brown	White
1	8	8	8
2	10	4	6
3	14	2	4
4	20	2	4

Which individuals have the highest fitness in this population?

Green

4. The pipe cleaners in the simulation of natural selection by predators gave birth to offspring that were the same color. Color in pipe cleaner populations is thus analogous to traits in natural populations that have a __*genetic*__ basis.

5. Is camouflage the only adaptation for surviving predation? Explain.

   No, certain species might evolve different strategies for surviving predation, including high rates of reproduction, increased speed, use of defensive structures or chemicals, and so on.

6. Traits that increase an individual's success at obtaining limited resources are favored by natural selection in environments where __*competition*__ is a major factor.

7. Do all mutations result in adaptations? Why or why not?

   No, some mutations can be harmful and result in traits that are selected against, and some can be neutral and not affected by natural selection.

8. Chickadees have a remarkable ability to learn from other birds about food sources they have never seen before. In fact, chickadees in the United Kingdom in the early 20th century learned how to drink out of milk bottles left on door stoops by milk delivery services. After one or a few chickadees learned how to do this, the ability spread throughout the countryside in a matter of months. Is drinking out of milk bottles an adaptation that is subject to evolution by natural selection in chickadees? Explain.

   No, the trait of drinking out of milk bottles is not an evolutionary adaptation, because the technique is learned, not passed on in the form of genes from one generation to the next. However, the ability to learn quickly is probably an adaptation in chickadees.

9. Imagine a dog that is born with a mutation that causes elongated and webbed feet. Is this an adaptation?

   Depends. The environment that the dog lives in will determine if this mutation leads to increased fitness—if it does, then it is an adaptation.

10. Use your understanding of natural selection to describe how the following trait might have evolved:

    Plants have pores on the surfaces of their leaves that allow carbon dioxide into the leaf (for photosynthesis), but also allow water to escape. Land plants have guard cells surrounding these pores that actively regulate the size of the pore and will make the pore smaller in dry conditions. The ancestors of land plants did not have guard cells.

    Because water is in limited supply on land, plants that had traits that helped to reduce water loss should have been favored by natural selection (as long as those traits did not overly interfere with the other functions of the plant). The ability of guard cells to actively regulate carbon dioxide uptake and water loss is an adaptation that allows land plants to maximize photosynthesis while minimizing water loss in a changing environment.

TOPIC 10

Species and Races

Learning Objectives

1. Describe the three steps required for the evolution of two new species from a single ancestor.
2. Apply an understanding of speciation to describe the origin of a pair of species.
3. Discuss the types of phenomena that lead to the isolation of gene pools within a species.
4. Define "biological race" and compare it to the definition of biological species.
5. Test whether populations of humans conform to the biological race concept.
6. Define the theory of convergent evolution and describe why convergent traits are not evidence of biological relationship.
7. Describe the process of sexual selection and compare and contrast this process with natural selection.
8. Describe the phenomenon of assortative mating and discuss how it reinforces human racial differences.
9. Discuss how assuming a biological basis for commonly described human racial categories can support racism.

A pre-laboratory quiz is available in Appendix A on page 215.

Instructors: This topic contains more material than can be covered in a single lab period. Exercises 10.5 and 10.6 can be combined with parts of the lab on natural selection (Topic 9) to make a lab on "types of selection."

Pre-laboratory Reading

A **biological species** is a group of individuals that, in nature, can interbreed and produce fertile offspring, but does not breed with members of another species. In other words, biological species are **reproductively isolated** from each other. According to theory, the evolution of two or more descendant species from a single ancestral species—**speciation**—can occur when subgroups, or **populations**, of the ancestral species become reproductively isolated. The formation of species generally requires three steps:

1. Isolation of the populations' **gene pools**, that is, the total set of alleles present in the population.
2. The occurrence of evoluti onary changes in one or more of the isolated populations.
3. The evolution of reproductive isolation between the populations, preventing the possibility of future **gene flow**, which is the movement of alleles from one population to another.

The gene pools of different populations can become isolated from each other for a number of reasons. A **physical** barrier might prevent contact between members of the different populations. This barrier might result from a geological event, such as the change in the course of a river, or it might result when a small population of individuals emigrates from the range of the main population. A **temporal**, or time-related, barrier also can stop gene flow among populations of species living in the same area; for instance, if subpopulations of migratory birds arrive at nesting sites at different times in the spring, most of the mating that occurs might be between individuals who have similar arrival times. After their gene pools have become isolated from each other, populations can follow divergent evolutionary paths; for example, if environmental conditions differ for populations in physically isolated environments, **natural selection** might favor one set of alleles in one environment and a different set in other environments. As isolated populations become more and more divergent from each other, individuals in the different populations might become reproductively incompatible; that is, they might be unable to mate because of large genetic or behavioral differences. Thus, the populations become reproductively isolated and will likely continue to become increasingly different from each other, even to the point of possessing completely different genes.

The period between the separation of gene pools and the evolution of reproductive isolation is when **biological races** of a species might form. Races can be thought of as populations of a single species that have diverged, but are not reproductively isolated, from each other. Often people assume that differences among groups or "races" of humans are mainly biological in nature; that is, that each race of humans represents a separate, and unique, evolutionary "line" of the human species. However, there is little evidence that "races" of humans are significantly different biologically.

In addition to the effects of natural selection, populations of organisms can diverge from each other as a result of **sexual selection**. Sexual selection has an effect on traits that influence mating success and is responsible for many of the differences between males and females of the same species. A widespread female preference for a particular trait in a male will cause that trait to become more prevalent in a population—and a widespread male preference is believed to cause females to evolve as well.

Differences among populations may be reinforced and maintained by **assortative mating**, in which individuals choose mates who are physically similar to them. When most people marry within their "racial" groups, the physical differences that help define the races remain distinct.

One factor that causes *unrelated* populations to resemble each other is called **convergent evolution**. Convergence occurs when populations are exposed to similar environmental factors and thus experience a similar regime of natural selection. In this case, both populations might *independently* evolve similar solutions to the environmental challenge. This is most easily seen in the similarities between dolphins and sharks. Superficially, dolphins and sharks appear very similar in body shape and color; however, dolphins are mammals and are more closely related to us than they are to their fish look-alikes. Similarities among human populations in skin color also appear to be a result of convergence of populations experiencing similar ultraviolet light levels.

Natural selection, sexual selection, and assortative mating have led to a variety of differences among human populations—convergent evolution has caused some of these populations to look more similar to each other than to other, equally unrelated, populations. However, as this lab will demonstrate, there are no consistent differences among human populations in different races or consistent similarities among human populations in the same race.

(45 Minutes)

Instructors: See Appendix B, page 239, for lab set-up information.
Materials:

- *Light microscopes, 1 per student pair*
- *Petri dishes containing* **Microbotryum** *crosses (see set-up info)*
- *Glass slides, 2–4 per student pair*
- *Forceps, 1 per student pair*
- *Water dropper bottle, 1 per student pair*
- *Cover slips*

Adapted from a lab written by Dr. Michael Hood, University of Virginia.

LAB EXERCISE 10.1

The Evolution of Reproductive Isolation

Microbotryum is a genus of fungi that causes plant diseases called "smuts." This fungus attacks the male organs (anthers) of affected plants, causing them to blacken and shrivel, resulting in male sterility. Insect pollinators who carry fungal spores from one plant to the other spread this disease. Traditionally, all anther smuts have been assumed to be caused by a single species of *Microbotryum*, but there is a real question about whether anther smut organisms found on different species of plants are in the process of becoming reproductively isolated from each other. This would occur if mating between strains that infect different flowers is unlikely, which might be the case if insect pollinators who carry the fungal spores tend to visit only one species of host flower, or if the host flower populations are geographically separated from each other.

A. Given what you have learned about the theory of how reproductive isolation evolves in separated populations, hypothesize about the degree of reproductive incompatibility among the following strains of *Microbotryum* crossed with the strain that attacks the flowers of *Silene latifolia* in Virginia. Consider both the geographic location of the host and its relatedness to *Silene latifolia* (see Table 10.1). Remember that the theory of evolution states that species in the same genus share a more recent common ancestor (and thus are more closely related to each other) than species in different genera.

TABLE 10.1

Microbotryum Strain Host Plant	Geographic Location of Host	Incompatibility with Strain infecting *Silene latifolia* in Virginia: Rank (1 = High, 6 = Low)
Silene latifolia	United Kingdom	
Silene latifolia	Virginia	
Silene caroliniana	North Carolina	
Silene virginica	Virginia	
Paspalum paniculatum	Costa Rica	
Lychnis flos-cuculi	United Kingdom	

B. Test your hypothesis.

1. Work in pairs for this exercise.
2. Obtain a petri dish containing developing fungi. Notice that the dish is marked and divided on the bottom into eight "pie pieces." Seven of these pie pieces contain a different cross between *Microbotryum* strains. The key to the labels is on Table 10.2. (Note: The (A1) and (A2) designations on the table refer to different "sexes" of the fungus. For sexual reproduction to occur, the two strains have to be of different sex.)

TABLE 10.2

Key	Cross (Name of Host Organism) *Silene latifolia* (A2) x	Number of Single Sporidia	Number of Conjugating Sporidia	Frequency of Conjugation
+C	*Silene latifolia* (A1)			
−C	*Silene latifolia* (A2)			
Sc	*Silene carolinana* (A1)			
SlUK	*Silene latifolia – UK* (A1)			
Sv	*Silene virginica* (A1)			
Sao	*Paspalum paniculatum* (A1)			
Lf	*Lychnis flos-cuculi* (A1)			

3. From each pie section, in turn, use a forceps to lift a small piece of agar that obviously contains fungal growth. Place this fragment face-up on a microscope slide, add a drop of water, and place a cover slip on it. Observe the slide under high power (20X or 40X) on a microscope stage.

4. You should observe many oval sacs on the agar. These are called sporidia. Some sporidia will be conjugating, meaning that a thin tube will be connecting adjacent sporidia. Ask your laboratory instructor for assistance if you are not certain you have identified a sporidium.

5. Start at one corner of the field of view and count the number of single and conjugating sporidia, up to 100 (or slightly more) total sporidia observed. Count each member of a conjugating pair as 1 sporidium. Enter your data in Table 10.2.

6. Calculate the frequency of conjugation by dividing the number of conjugating sporidia by the total number of sporidia observed.

C. Discuss the following questions and be prepared to share your answers with your lab instructor and classmates.

1. Do crosses between different strains show differing amounts of reproductive compatibility as indicated by conjugation frequency?

2. What is the purpose of the "+C" cross (which also could be called the "positive control")?

   Establishes that media is appropriate for growth and conjugation. Provides a baseline that illustrates the maximum number of conjugating sporidia expected under these experimental conditions when the mating strains are completely reproductively compatible.

3. What is the purpose of the "−C" cross (which could be called the "negative control")?

   Provides a comparison that illustrates the number of conjugating sporidia expected under the conditions of the experiment when the mating strains are completely reproductively incompatible.

4. Did the results of the experimental crosses support your hypothesis?

5. Explain why the strains of *Microbotryum* found on different plants might be diverging from each other.

   *Different host species might have different flowering times, which would restrict gene flow among **Microbotryum** strains. Geographic isolation among the plants would allow different strains to diverge. Additionally, differing selective pressures on different host species might cause divergence among strains.*

6. Do the strains of *Microbotryum* on different plants appear to be different biological species? Do they appear to be different biological races? Support your answer.

   They probably will not appear to be different species—all crosses can form conjugating sporidia, although there are differences in compatibility, indicating that they are possibly different biological races. However, we don't know if the conjugating sporidia produce successful offspring by these observations, so we still do not know if reproductive isolation exists.

(30 Minutes)

Materials: Photos of people demonstrating a wide range of human diversity. The following websites contain a nice diversity of photos:

- http://www.aarongang.com/headshots/index1.htm
- http://frickphotography.com/men.html
- http://frickphotography.com/women.html
- http://www.hollywoodheadshotstudio.com/hsg1.html

LAB EXERCISE 10.2

The Morphological Basis of Human Race Classifications

People often assume that a set of physical (that is, **morphological**) characteristics unites groups of individuals within the major human races. In this series of exercises, you will use a number of photographs of people to investigate whether humans are easily classified into races and whether the morphological differences among these races are as distinct as we might assume.

A. Group people into racial categories.

1. Work together with your lab partners to classify the people in the photographs provided into races.

2. After you have completed your groupings, fill in Table 10.3. Give the groups names (for example, Asians, Hispanics, and so on). For each grouping, write the name and the *physical characteristics* that the members of the group share, as evidenced by the photographs. Be as specific as possible when describing the physical traits. You might have more or fewer groupings than table rows.

One user of this manual downloaded photos from these sources into a PowerPoint slide show, then viewed them using the "Slide View" option of the program, which allows students to rearrange them into groups.

The authors of this manual have used a set of postcards produced by National Geographic called "Portraits" published by Phaidon Press in 1999. As of press time, this collection was still available on Amazon.com and the publisher's own website. Each group of students should receive copies of the same 35–40 photos. Instructors: Students should stick to observable physical characteristics only. No assumptions about unseen characteristics are allowable.

TABLE 10.3

Group Name	Physical Traits

B. Discuss the following questions and be prepared to share your answers with your lab instructor and classmates.

1. Look at the groupings made by other lab tables. Did everyone in the lab group people identically?

2. Discuss the physical traits you used to make your groupings. Were there some key traits that other groups used to classify these individuals that you did not?

3. Were there individuals you found difficult to classify? Why? What additional information would have been useful?

C. Make a closer examination of the traits we use to group people into races. Take the same pictures you used in part A and arrange them in a line by skin color only. Photos should be arranged to show a gradient from darkest to lightest skin (if people appear to be the same shade, stack the pictures together).

D. Discuss the following questions and be prepared to share your answers with your lab instructor and classmates.

1. Are all the individuals in each race you described in part A next to each other in the line, or are the groups mixed together?

2. Are clear "breaks" between people with different skin color types apparent, or is the variation **continuous** (that is, does skin color change gradually as you move along the line)?

3. If you chose another trait to arrange people by (say eye or nose shape), would arrangement of individuals be the same?

4. What does your answer to the previous question tell you about correlation among morphological (physical) characters in people? In other words, do all people with darker skin have one typical nose shape while those with lighter skin have another different shape?

5. The groupings you made in part A of this exercise reflected your feelings about the key morphological traits that define the race of an individual. Why do you think these traits are more important than other traits in determining someone's racial identity?

(45 Minutes)

Materials:

- *Map of world with skin colors of indigenous human populations indicated. See page 240 in Appendix B. Source: Jablonski, N.J. and G. Chaplin, 2000. The evolution of human skin coloration.* **Journal of Human Evolution** *39: 57-106 (Figure 3). 1 per student group.*
- *World map with political boundaries and country names labeled. 1 per student group.*
- *Transparency sheets with outline of major continents from above map. 3 per student group.*
- *Multiple colors of washable marking pens*

Instructors: You can acquire additional allele frequency data for a number of genes in a number of different populations from the following Web resource: http://alfred.med.yale.edu/ alfred/index.asp.

LAB EXERCISE 10.3

Are Human Races Biological Races?

We can consider the commonly used racial categories (for example, American Indian, Asian, Black, Pacific Islander, White) as a hypothesis; that is, that human populations grouped together in these races are more similar biologically, or share a more recent common ancestor, than human populations in different races. One way to test this hypothesis is to look for nonmorphological similarities among populations within a race. In this exercise, you will investigate whether populations with similar skin colors (and thus assumed to be the same race) are similar in other, less visible traits.

A. Is skin color a mark of shared evolutionary history?

1. On the following pages, you will find a series of data tables (Tables 10.4, 10.5, and 10.6) containing information about gene frequencies in different human population groups.

2. For each gene described, you should create a different map using the transparency maps available. Color regions of the maps corresponding to the allele frequency group populations in that region. (In other words, all populations in the "High A, High B" group should be the same color, while all populations in the "Low A, No B" group should be a different color.) Overlay these transparent maps and the map of skin color distribution to answer the discussion questions.

Note: These maps will be incomplete. Collecting data on allele frequencies in populations is time consuming and of limited scientific interest. Thus, very few genes have been evaluated, and for no genes have allele frequencies been calculated in all human populations.

TABLE 10.4 **ABO Blood Types**

People	Place
Low A, no B	
Toba Indians	Argentina
Sioux Indians	South Dakota
Moderate A, no B	
Navaho Indians	New Mexico
Pueblo Indians	New Mexico, Northern Mexico
High A, little B	
Blood Indians	Montana
Australian Aborigines	Southern Australia
Inuit	Northern Canada
Basques	France and Spain
Shoshone Indians	Wyoming
Polynesians	Hawaii
Fairly high A, some B	
English	England
French	France
Armenians	Turkey
Lapps	Northern Finland
Melanesians	New Guinea
Germans	Germany
High A, high B	
Welsh	Wales, Great Britain
Italians	Italy
Siamese	Thailand
Finns	Southern Finland
Ukrainians	Ukraine
Indians	India

TABLE 10.5   **PTC Tasters**

People	Place
Less than 10%	
Chinese	Taiwan
Cree Indians	Northern Central Canada
Chinese	China
Africans	West Africa
Bantu	Kenya
Lapps	Finland
Japanese	Japan
11–20%	
Chilean	Chile
Malayan	Malaysia
Hindu	Northern India
Cabocio Indians	Brazil
21–30%	
Belgian	Belgium
Portuguese	Portugal
Inuit	Northern Alaska
Arabs	Sudan
Finns	Finland
Hindu	Southern India
31% and greater	
Norwegians	Norway
English	England
Eskimos	Labrador
Danes	Denmark

TABLE 10.6   **Lactase Deficiency**

People	Place
75% or more are deficient	
Papunya	Australia
Chami	Colombia
Chinese	China
Bantu	Central Africa
Thai	Thailand
Lapps	Northern Finland
Less than 70% are deficient	
Batutsi	Rwanda, Sub Saharan Africa
Eskimos	Greenland
Indian (no tribe designated)	North America
Finns	Southern Finland

B. Discuss the following questions and be prepared to share your answers with your lab instructor and classmates.

1. Does it appear that shared skin color is an indication of other shared nonmorphological traits?

2. Does shared skin color seem to indicate common ancestry? Why or why not?

3. Relate this exercise back to Lab Exercise 10.2. Does it appear that the groups you made in that exercise reflect distinct biological populations? Why or why not?

LAB EXERCISE 10.4

Discuss Biology and Racism

(20 Minutes)

Instructors: Chapter 6 in the accompanying textbook reviews **The Bell Curve** *and some of its flaws in more detail. If you are using the textbook, you might want to assign reading from that chapter before this discussion.*

A. Read the following summary.

In 1994, *The Bell Curve*, a book by Richard J. Herrnstein and Charles Murray, was published. It quickly became a bestseller and the focus of intense controversy. In *The Bell Curve*, Herrnstein and Murray argued that affirmative action programs (that is, programs that preferentially award jobs, scholarships, and so on to members of racial groups that are under-represented in leadership positions) are doomed to failure because racial groups differ in their innate intelligence. One of the authors' most controversial statements was that black Americans have lower IQs than white Americans, on average, because blacks have genes that result in lower intelligence than whites.

B. Discuss the following questions and be prepared to share your answers with your lab instructor and classmates.

1. Given what you have learned in Lab Exercise 10.3 about the relationship between shared skin color and other genetic traits, do you think it is reasonable to group all blacks together into one biological group, as Herrnstein and Murray did? Why or why not?

2. Racism is basically the idea that some groups of people are better than others, and that it is somehow justified or proper for the more powerful group to subdue and oppress the less powerful. Is a book like *The Bell Curve* racist itself? Does it contribute to racist beliefs?

(30 Minutes)

Materials: Personal ads. Many major city news-papers have extensive personals. Seek out those that have the style of describing both the adver-tiser and the traits that the advertiser seeks in a date. Ideally, you should have on hand a number of pages of ads, so that different student groups are reviewing different materials.

LAB EXERCISE 10.5

Investigate Sexual Selection

As discussed in the pre-laboratory reading, theory states that sexual selection causes the evolution of traits that are related to mating success. Differences among human populations in how individuals choose mates can lead to differences among them in physical traits. However, sexual selection also appears to lead to differences in the preferences and behaviors of males and females in many species.

Sexual selection theory states that males and females should have different reproductive strategies and therefore should favor different characters in their mates. In general, males in species that are polygamous (that is, where individuals have more than one partner) are hypothesized to be primarily interested in the youth and health of their potential mates—younger, healthier females are more likely to produce healthy offspring than older females, and the reproductive success of males is maximized by the total number of offspring they father.

The reproductive success of females is not just a function of the number of offspring they produce, which is limited because producing offspring is so energy intensive for females, but by the "quality" of those offspring in terms of their ability to survive and reproduce themselves. Thus females are hypothesized to be generally more interested in the genetic quality of their mates and the ability of these mates to provide resources for the developing offspring.

Biologists debate whether sexual selection theory can explain the behavior of human males and females, and if it can, how well. In this exercise, you will investigate whether there is evidence that human behavior conforms to sexual selection theory.

A. Do men and women have different preferences for mates?

1. Given the previous description of how males and females differ, hypothesize about what traits or qualities men would be expected to favor in a potential mate and what traits or qualities women would be expected to favor in a potential mate. List these traits in Table 10.7.

TABLE 10.7

Traits Men Should Favor in Mates	Traits Women Should Favor in Mates

2. Choose two traits from each column in Table 10.7 that you think are likely to be "requested" in personal ads published in standard newspapers. Write these traits in the first column of Table 10.8.
3. Obtain a page of personal ads from your laboratory instructor.
4. Carefully read the ads in the "men seeking women" and the "women seeking men" categories (or a number specified by your lab instructor, if the listing is very long). If one of the four traits you identified appears in an ad, note this with a check mark in the appropriate cell on the table.

TABLE 10.8

Expected Mate Preferences in Ads	Number of times the preference appears in "Men Seeking Women" ads	Number of times the preference appears in "Women Seeking Men" ads
Traits expected to be preferred by Men Seeking Women		
1.		
2.		
Traits expected to be preferred by Women Seeking Men		
3.		
4.		

B. Discuss the following questions and be prepared to share the answers with your lab instructor and classmates.

   1. Did the results of your survey of the personal ads support the hypothesis that men and women seek different traits in potential mates? Why or why not? Consider the function of personal ads and that the hypothesis applies to polygamous species. Are humans polygamous?

   2. Did you notice any additional patterns in the personal ads that might indicate differences between women and men in their mate preferences?

   3. Given that differences among human populations are partially a result of differences in traits valued by men and women in each population, do you think personal ads in other cultures might "read" differently? Give some examples.

   4. Do you think evaluating personal ads is an adequate way to evaluate the preferences of men and women for mates? Why or why not?

   5. If patterns in the personal ads are a reflection of how sexual selection occurs in a modern human population, do you think that men and women are continuing to evolve? Given what you have read, what sorts of traits would you expect to become more common in men? In women?

(30 Minutes)

Materials: Personal ads. Many major city newspapers have extensive personals. Seek out those that have the style of describing both the advertiser and the traits that the advertiser seeks in a date. Ideally, you should have on hand a number of pages of ads, so that different student groups are reviewing different materials.

Instructors: Lab exercises 10.5 and 10.6 can both be extended by performing an analysis of wedding announcements published in the newspaper. It can be interesting to compare whether preferences expressed in "ideal mate" ads are reflected in "real mate" relationships. Analysis of these announcements, however, can be a bit more difficult—race and other physical traits often have to be guessed from a photo, and information about age or professional status can be more challenging to obtain from written descriptions of the bride and groom.

LAB EXERCISE 10.6

Investigate Assortative Mating

A. Do men and women seek mates who are like themselves?

Personal ads contain information about the physical traits and often the educational/occupational status of the ad's writer as well as the physical traits and educational/occupational status of the mates that are being sought. We can use these advertisements to determine whether men and women desire partners who are similar to them in a number of traits.

1. Obtain a page of personal ads from your laboratory instructor. In many personals, descriptors of race, religion, marital status, and professional status are indicated in a shorthand manner (for example, "BF" might mean "black female"). Find the key that helps explain these categories.

2. Looking at the key, choose three general descriptors (for example, race, divorced versus single, religion specified) that ad writers use to classify themselves and their ideal mates. Write these in the first column of Table 10.9.

TABLE 10.9

General Descriptor	A. Ideal Mate Same as Ad Writer	B. Ideal Mate Different from Ad Writer	C. Did Not Specify Single Preferred Trait in Ideal Mate	D. Total Ads (A + B + C)

3. Examine the ads carefully and record on the table whether advertisers sought mates similar to themselves on the three descriptors you specified previously, different from themselves, or if they did not specify (or specified multiple preferences).

4. Determine the percent of individuals displaying a preference for positive assortative mating for each descriptor by dividing the number in column A by the number in column D. Record this result in Table 10.10.

5. Determine the percent of individuals displaying a preference for negative assortative mating for each descriptor by dividing the number in column B by the number in column D. Record this result in Table 10.10.

TABLE 10.10

General Descriptor	Percent with Positive Assortative Mating Preference	Percent with Negative Assortative Mating Preference

B. Discuss the following questions and be prepared to share your answers with your lab instructor and classmates.

1. Of the three traits you chose for this exercise, which appeared to be most important to advertisers? In other words, which were specified in the largest number of ads?

2. Were advertisers interested in finding mates like themselves or unlike themselves on these important traits?

3. Discuss the traits (if any) that appeared to be less important (as measured by the number of individuals who mentioned the trait). What is the difference between important traits and less important ones? Were individuals showing a positive assortative mating preference for these traits or a negative one?

4. Consider your answers to the previous questions. Does assortative mating appear likely to be reinforcing physical differences between human populations? What about social differences?

TOPIC 10
_____

POST-LABORATORY QUIZ

SPECIES AND RACES

1. In the cross of fungal strains of different sexes found on different hosts, what observation would convince you that these two strains are actually different species?

   No sexual reproduction between the strains.

2. Given the results of the crossing experiment between different strains of anther smut, how might you expect the outcome of crosses between individuals of different human races should turn out, if these races represent true biological races?

   Crosses between individuals of different human races should be more rare than crosses within races, and there should be fewer successful offspring produced by these crosses.

3. Skin color in humans is continuously variable. What does this mean?

   Skin color grades from very light to very dark among individual humans and individual human populations, with few or no "breaks" in the color distribution.

4. Is shared skin color among human populations correlated to other shared morphological traits? Explain your answer.

   Based on the analysis of the photos in this lab, it does not appear to be closely correlated with other traits. In other words, many different face shapes, nose shapes, eye shapes, and hair types are found within each human skin color group.

5. Are populations of humans who share the same skin color similar "underneath the skin" as well? Explain your answer.

   No, according to the data on allele frequencies in different human populations. Many populations that have similar skin color have very different allele frequencies for other genes.

6. Human populations that share a similar skin color might appear similar as a result of convergent evolution. What is convergent evolution?

   Convergent evolution is the independent evolution of superficially similar traits in different populations. This typically occurs when populations have similarities in their environments, even if they are not related to each other.

7. Why are females expected to prefer different traits in their potential mates than males prefer in their mates?

The reproductive success of a female depends on the quality of her offspring, while the reproductive success of a male is more dependent on the number of offspring he produces.

8. If modern humans choose their mates as predicted by sexual selection theory, what sorts of traits should women desire in men?

Women should seek men who display high quality—in our society, this is probably best measured by earning potential.

9. Does positive assortative mating for skin color and ethnic background reinforce or dilute differences among human races? Explain your answer.

Positive assortative mating occurs when individuals choose mates who are similar to themselves. This would tend to reinforce differences among human races by reducing "mixing" among individuals with different alleles for skin color and different social traditions.

10. What is racism?

The belief that one group of humans is superior to other groups of humans, and that the differences between human groups are innate (for example, fixed in the genes).

TOPIC 11

Biodiversity

Learning Objectives

1. Describe the distinction between domain and kingdom.
2. Describe the characteristics of the major categories of living organisms.
3. Describe how the classification system appears to reflect the relationships among modern organisms.
4. Practice using a dichotomous key.
5. Gain an appreciation for the diversity of life on Earth.

A pre-laboratory quiz is available in Appendix A on page 217.

Pre-laboratory Reading

The term **biodiversity** encapsulates the great variety of life—from the diversity of alleles within a species, to the diversity of species on the planet. Biodiversity is part of what makes biology a fascinating and continually developing science. In this set of lab exercises, we review a tiny sample of the many forms of life on Earth. The exercises that make up this small sampling are too numerous for a single lab period—your laboratory instructor has had to make some tough decisions about how to cover this small sampling of biodiversity within time constraints. To put into perspective the impossibility of surveying life in a single lab period, consider the following: If we were to spend five seconds viewing every species on Earth that has been identified (about 1.8 million), it would take us over three months of solid observation to see them all. And, if estimates about the actual number of species are correct (more than 200 million), it would take more than 30 years!

To organize the study of diversity, biologists have developed a **classification system** that categorizes organisms into similar groups. The largest subdivision in the current system is called the **domain**. All living organisms can be classified into one of three great domains of life that are distinguished by fundamental differences in cell structure. The next largest subdivision is the **kingdom**. Only one domain currently has well-defined kingdoms, which categorize organisms based on similarities in cell structure and mode of nutrition. The most widely used classification of living organisms divides life into three domains and four kingdoms. Our survey of diversity uses this classification system as a way to give a broad overview of the variety of life:

Instructors: This topic contains more exercises than can comfortably fit in a single typical lab period of two to three hours. We have provided an abundance and diversity of activities to give you many options for creating a lab or series of labs that best fit your goals and objectives.

Domains

Bacteria Single-celled organisms without a nucleus and with cell walls containing **peptidoglycan,** a complex of protein and sugars. Although some bacteria cause disease, many are benign or beneficial to humans.

Archaea Single-celled organisms without a nucleus and with cell walls that do not contain peptidoglycan. Many of the known species grow in extreme environments, such as very salty or very high-temperature water.

Eukarya (see following kingdom descriptions) Organisms made up of cells with a membrane-bound nucleus that contains the genetic material of the cell. This is the only domain containing truly **multicellular** organisms; that is, those containing cells that are integrated and specialized for specific functions.

Kingdoms of Eukarya:

Protista (amoeba, algae, diatoms) All organisms in this group have a free-living single cell stage for at least part of their life cycle. Most are unicellular, such as amoebae and paramecia, but many of the algae have a multicellular, stationary phase (such as kelp).

Plantae (plants) Multicellular organisms that are **autotrophic** (make their own food).

Fungi (fungi, molds, yeast) Multicellular organisms that are **heterotrophic** (rely on other organisms for food), digest food outside of their bodies, and absorb the products of digestion.

Animalia (animals) Multicellular organisms that are heterotrophic and ingest food for digestion inside the body.

The four kingdoms and two noneukarya domains are further classified into smaller groups as follows, from most- to least-inclusive:

Phylum
  Class
    Order
      Family
        Genus
          Species

For instance, in the kingdom Animalia, all species that produce an external skeleton are placed in the phylum Arthropoda. Within this phylum, all species that have three major body segments (a head, thorax or "chest", and abdomen) are placed in the class Insecta. Within the Insecta, all species that produce two hardened wings that form a protective covering for the two membranous wings beneath them are placed in the same order, Coleoptera—the beetles.

Our ability to group organisms into categories that reflect greater and greater degrees of similarity is considered evidence that living organisms are related to each other. In other words, the reason all species in the Order Coleoptera have similar wings is because they all derived from an ancestral species that had this type of wings. In fact, Charles Darwin used the pattern of similarity that drove the development of this classification system as one piece of evidence for the **theory of evolution**—the theory that all organisms alive today represent the descendants of a single ancestral species that arose on Earth billions of years ago.

(Parts A–C, 30 Minutes; Part D, 10 Minutes)

LAB EXERCISE 11.1

The Relationship Among the Domains of Life

A simplified version of Woese's tree is available in Appendix B on page 241.

If all modern organisms derived from a common ancestor in the past and if more similar species share a more recent common ancestor, we should be able to picture the relationships among living organisms as a tree containing a series of branching events. In this exercise, you will generate and test a hypothesis about the relationship among the three domains of life.

A. Examine the generic tree in Figure 11.1. This tree contains all of the major elements required when illustrating a hypothesis of evolutionary relationship among organisms.

B. Discuss the following question with your lab partners and be prepared to share your answer:

  1. Domain 2 and Domain 3 are hypothesized to share a more recent common ancestor with each other than either does with Domain 1. What observations would cause a scientist to make this hypothesis?

    There are a greater number of similarities between species in domain 2 and domain 3 than between species in domain 2 and domain 1 or between species in domain 3 and domain 1. We can assume that traits that are similar between domains 2 and 3, but different from domain 1, evolved in the common ancestor of domains 2 and 3 after divergence from its common ancestor with domain 1.

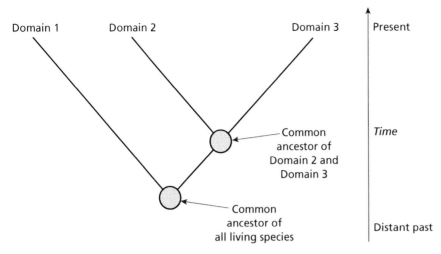

FIGURE 11.1

C. Given Table 11.1 of characteristics found in the three domains, work with your lab partners to create a hypothesis of evolutionary relationship among these groups. Basically, the more characteristics two domains share, the more likely they are to share a more recent common ancestor. Be prepared to share your hypothesis and to explain your reasoning.

D. Test your hypothesis.

   The hypothesis of evolutionary relationship represented by the tree you have just drawn can be tested via other data. In 1977, the biologist Carl Woese compared the DNA sequences of the gene that codes for part of the ribosome (the organelle that is responsible for translating DNA information into proteins) among a large number of species. The tree that Woese generated based on these DNA sequences is often called the "universal **phylogeny**" or universal family tree.

   1. Use the resources available to you (for example, your textbook, the Internet, other biology texts) to locate a reproduction of Carl Woese's universal phylogeny.

TABLE 11.1

Characteristic	Bacteria	Archaea	Eukarya
Nucleus present	No	No	Yes
Cell contains internal structures surrounded by a membrane	No	No	Yes
Cell wall contains peptidoglycan	Yes	No	No
Type of RNA polymerase (that is, transcription enzyme)	One	Several	Several
Response to antibiotics streptomycin and chloramphenicol	Growth inhibited	Growth not inhibited	Growth not inhibited
Histone proteins associated with DNA	No	Yes	Yes
Circular chromosome	Yes	Yes	No
Genes contain DNA sequences that do not code for protein (that is, introns)	No	Some	Yes
Amino acid that initiates translation	Formyl-methionine	Methionine	Methionine
Ability to grow at temperatures exceeding 100° C	No	Some species	No

2. Compare the tree you generated to Woese's tree. Does his tree support your hypothesis? Why or why not?

Student answers to this question will depend on the tree they generated initially.

(Part A, 15 Minutes; Part B, 30 Minutes – or 15 If Prepared Slides Used)

Instructor: Laboratory Topic 2 in this manual provides a brief introduction to the parts of the microscope and its use.

This exercise could also be set up as a demonstration, although students are interested in what they find on their own teeth.
Materials:
- *Sterile cotton swab*
- *Microscope slide*
- *250-mL beaker*
- *100% methanol (alternative, Bunsen burner – for fixing bacteria to slide)*
- *Crystal violet stain*
- *Light microscope with 100 × objective*
- *Immersion oil*

Materials:
- **Escherichia coli** *(Gram negative) and 4 different antibiotic sensitivity disks on antibiotic agar (Petri dishes, 15 × 100 mm), 1 per lab section*
- **Staphylococcus aureus** *(Gram positive) and 4 different antibiotic sensitivity disks on antibiotic agar (Petri dishes, 15 × 100 mm), 1 per lab section*
- *At least 4 kinds of antibiotic disks, 1 should be penicillin or ampicillin (available from biological suppliers)*
- *Glass slides*
- *Sterile toothpicks*
- *Dropper bottles of distilled water*
- *250-mL beakers*
- *100% methanol OR Bunsen burner*
- *Crystal violet*
- *Iodine*
- *Gram Decolorizer*
- *Safranin*
- *Paper towels*
- *Light microscopes with 100 × objectives*
- *Immersion oil*

Instructors: The bacterial cultures must be no older than 24 hours in order to stain correctly. Gram-positive bacteria will appear Gram negative if they are "old" cells.
Note: As an alternative to having students perform the Gram stain procedure, you could supply prepared Gram-stained slides of E. coli and S. aureus.
See Appendix B, page 242, for an alternative Gram stain protocol.

LAB EXERCISE 11.2

A Survey of the Domains Bacteria and Archaea

A. Visualize the abundance of bacteria in the environment.

1. With a sterile cotton swab, obtain a sample of bacteria from your teeth. Gently rub the swab over the surfaces of several back teeth.

2. Carefully roll the swab across the surface of a clean glass slide. Try to spread the material thinly and evenly.

3. Place the slide across the top of the beaker and allow the smear to air dry.

4. Flood the smear with methanol for one minute OR quickly pass the slide through a flame (right side up) two or three times. Allow the smear to air dry before staining.

5. Bring the slide and beaker to a sink and carefully flood the slide with crystal violet. This stain is messy and permanently dyes fabric—avoid contact with your clothes and skin and wipe up any spills thoroughly. Wait one to two minutes and then rinse the slide with cold tap water.

6. Gently shake off the excess water and allow the smear to air dry.

7. Focus on the smear using the lower power objective lens, then observe the slide under the highest power microscope objective, adjusting focus only with the fine adjustment knob on the scope.

8. Estimate the number of bacterial cells that are visible in a field of view.

_____

9. Estimate the size of the smear on the slide. _____

10. Calculate the number of bacteria you collected on the swab.

Number of bacteria in field of view × size of smear = _____

B. Investigate the function of antibiotics.

Domain Bacteria contains many infamous members, including the organisms that cause tuberculosis, syphilis, gonorrhea, anthrax, cholera, tetanus, and leprosy, not to mention all manner of food poisoning and blood-borne infections. Yet in the larger picture, only a very small proportion of bacteria cause disease—most do not affect us at all or are beneficial to us.

The presence of **pathogenic** (disease-causing) bacteria and the severity of diseases they cause have driven interest in the development of drugs that selectively target and kill bacteria—generally called **antibiotics**. The presence of the unique compound peptidoglycan in bacterial cell walls provides a means for antibiotics to target bacterial cells without harming our own body cells. The antibiotic penicillin prevents the synthesis of peptidoglycan, thus preventing the growth of bacterial populations.

There is variation among bacterial species in their susceptibility to antibiotics. We can divide the bacterial domain into two major groups of bacteria: those with simple peptidoglycan cell walls and those with peptidoglycan cell walls surrounded by a membrane. The outer membrane on the latter type of bacteria impedes the movement of materials into the cells. As you might imagine, this type of bacterium tends to be less sensitive to antibiotics such as penicillin. However, broad-spectrum antibiotics exist that are toxic to both kinds of bacteria. These antibiotics tend to have more severe side effects in patients than the narrower-spectrum antibiotics.

1. Observe the two plates of bacteria available in lab. You should note the disks impregnated with antibiotic present on the surface of these plates.

If the bacteria on the dish are susceptible to the antibiotic, a clear area will appear around the disk—if not, bacteria will grow up to the surface of the disk, causing a cloudy appearance. Fill in Table 11.2, noting which bacterial species are susceptible to which antibiotic:

TABLE 11.2

	Antibiotic A Name:	Antibiotic B Name:	Antibiotic C Name:	Antibiotic D Name:
Bacterial Species 1 Name:				
Bacterial Species 2 Name:				

2. Given what you have learned about the two groups of bacteria, make a hypothesis about which type of cell wall you expect to find in:

   Bacterial Species 1 _____

   Bacterial Species 2 _____

3. The two types of bacteria respond differently to a cell-staining procedure known as the Gram stain. You can test the hypothesis you made in step 2 by performing a Gram stain on the two bacterial species using the following protocol:

   a. Obtain a clean glass slide and place a single drop of distilled water in the center of the slide.
   b. Use a clean toothpick to obtain a <u>tiny</u> sample of the bacterial culture from one of the petri dishes.
   c. Gently stir the toothpick in the water on the glass slide. Spread the water into a thin layer.
   d. Place the slide on the beaker and allow it to air dry. Bring the slide and beaker to a sink for the staining process.
   e. Flood the smear with methanol for 1 minute OR pass the slide through a flame (right side up) two or three times. Allow the smear to dry before staining.
   f. Flood the smear with crystal violet, and wait for 1–2 minutes. (Note: this and the other stains can permanently mar clothing. Avoid spills, and clean any promptly and thoroughly.)
   g. Gently rinse off the crystal violet with cold tap water.
   h. Flood the smear with iodine and wait for 1 minute.
   i. Gently rinse off the iodine with cold tap water.
   j. Rinse the smear with Gram Decolorizer until the solution rinses colorless from the slide (5 seconds).
   k. Immediately rinse the smear with cold water.
   l. Flood the smear with safranin and allow it to stain for 15–30 seconds.
   m. Gently rinse with cold tap water.
   n. Blot off excess water with a paper towel, and allow the smear to air dry.
   o. Repeat the same procedure with the second bacterial culture.
   p. Wash your hands thoroughly when finished.

   Bacterial cells that have the simple peptidoglycan cell wall will pick up the violet stain and will remain violet in color throughout the rest of the preparation—these cells are called Gram-positive bacteria. Those bacteria with the additional outer membrane outside the wall do not keep the violet stain throughout the procedure, but will stain with the second dye, the red safranin—these cells are called Gram-negative bacteria.

4. Examine the slides microscopically and record your observations in Table 11.3.

TABLE 11.3

	Gram positive or negative?
Bacteria Species 1	
Bacteria Species 2	

5. Do these observations support the hypothesis you made in step 2 of this exercise?

6. Which of the antibiotics used in this exercise appear to be broad-spectrum antibiotics?

(Time required depends on number of specimens available)

Materials:
- *Light microscopes*
- *Prepared slides of a variety of protists (for example: **Oomycota, Trypanosoma, Plasmodium, Volvox**)*
- *Clean microscope slides*
- *Cultures of a variety of microscopic protists (for example: **Amoeba, Paramecium, Stentor, Spirogyra, Euglena**)*
- *Droppers*
- *Methyl-cellulose*
- *Samples of multicellular protists (for example: **Fucus, Sargassum, Corallina, Physarum**)*

LAB EXERCISE 11.3

A Survey of the Kingdom Protista

A. Observe various members of the kingdom Protista.

The protists are a mixed bag of highly diverse organisms. In general, we can group the members of this kingdom into three broad "functional groups": (1) the plant-like protists that make their own food, (2) the animal-like protists that are highly motile and engulf food, and (3) the fungus-like protists, which are often less motile and tend to dissolve their food source before absorbing its now-simplified nutrients.

1. Examine the variety of protists available in the laboratory. Based on your observations, attempt to determine the basic life style of each and record your determinations in Table 11.4. Be prepared to share your answers (and your rationale) with your lab instructor and classmates.

TABLE 11.4

Protist	Plant-like, Animal-like, or Fungus-like?	What Is Your Evidence?

B. Investigate whether human activities in an environment affect the diversity of protists in that environment.

1. Collect water and some sediment from two different ponds. One should be a storm water retention pond, such as those found near parking lots and other developments, while the other should be a natural pond in a park or protected area.

2. Mix the water and sediment thoroughly and prepare a wet mount of each pond sample by placing a drop of liquid on a slide, adding a drop of methyl cellulose to slow down the movement of the organisms, and covering it with a coverslip.

3. As best as you can, determine the number of different protistan species you can see in each drop of water. You do not need to identify these by their scientific name, simply keep track of how many different types you see. A sketch or brief description on the following table will help you in this task.

4. Now count the number of individuals of each type you have identified and fill in Table 11.5.

Time required depends on whether a field trip is involved. If samples available in lab, 40 minutes. If field trip, entire lab period.

Materials:
- *Collecting jars (alternatively, water from two ponds, including some sediment, collected earlier in the day and made available in lab. For best results, fresh samples should be obtained each day.)*
- *Eye droppers*
- *Glass slides*
- *Methyl cellulose in dropper bottles*
- *Cover slips*
- *Light microscopes*
- *Calculators*

TABLE 11.5

Pond 1:	Number Observed (A)	Number Observed – 1 (B)	A × B	Pond 2:	Number Observed (A)	Number Observed – 1 (B)	A × B
Species:				Species:			
Species:				Species:			
Species:				Species:			
Species:				Species:			
Species:				Species:			
Species:				Species:			
Species:				Species:			
Species:				Species:			
Species:				Species:			
Species:				Species:			
Species:				Species:			
Sum of Column (A × B)				Sum of Column (A × B)			

5. Complete the following calculations of the "diversity index" for each pond site and fill in Table 11.6:

$$\frac{\text{Total number of species seen} \times (\text{Total number of species seen} - 1)}{\text{Sum of Column (A} \times \text{B)}}$$

TABLE 11.6

	Diversity Index
Pond 1:	
Pond 2:	

6. The diversity indexes in the preceding table allow you to compare the diversity in the two ponds as measured both by number of species (a measure called **species richness**) and abundance of species. By dividing a measure of the number of species you observed in each environment by a measure of the abundance of each species observed, you will generate a number that tells you whether one or a few species dominate in that environment. Basically, having a large number of species leads to a greater diversity, but if nearly every individual in an environment belongs to a single species and there are only a few individuals in the remaining species, the environment is actually not very diverse. A larger diversity index equates to greater diversity.

7. Describe your results. Which environment has a more diverse protistan fauna? Why do you think this is the case?

(15 Minutes)

Materials:
See Appendix B, page 243, for a list and description of the most common animal phyla.

LAB EXERCISE 11.4

A Survey of the Kingdom Animalia

A. Discuss the diversity of the animal kingdom.

Most people's conception of what constitutes an "animal" is surprisingly limited. Recent classifications identify 35 animal phyla, but nearly all animals we think of belong to three or four of these.

1. Keeping in mind the basic definition of "animal"—multicellular organisms that make their living by ingesting other organisms and which are motile during at least one stage of their life cycle—brainstorm a list of animals with your lab partners. Be prepared to share this list with your lab instructor and classmates.

2. With the help of your lab instructor, determine the number of different animal phyla represented on your list. How many phyla are represented by the class's list?

B. Learn the characteristics of some common animal phyla and practice using a dichotomous key.

(30 Minutes)

Materials:
- *Models and figures of various animal phyla*
- *A number of living and preserved specimens of animals, from a variety of phyla*

Instructors: Ensure that there are examples (either whole or diagrams) of the body forms, skeletons, and digestive systems described in the upcoming paragraphs, and that nearly all "unknown" animals can be correctly keyed out to phyla. We have found it somewhat instructive to have a few examples that do not key out easily (for example, squid do not readily key out to Mollusca on this key), in order to illustrate the challenge of constructing a dichotomous key that is fail-proof, but you should avoid having too many ambiguous specimens.

Animals are grouped into phyla based on shared body form, skeleton type, and digestive system. We assume that animals present today that are similar in these three traits are all descendants of a single species that had these same traits.

1. Examine the models and diagrams available in the lab to understand the differences in body form, skeleton type, and digestive system (described next) that are found in modern animals.

Body forms are typically described in terms of symmetry:

asymmetry Lack of symmetry, the animal cannot be cut along an axis that creates two mirror images.

radial symmetry Has a top, a bottom, and a central axis, meaning it can be cut into many equal and identical parts (like a cake or pie).

bilateral symmetry Has a top, bottom, left side, right side, head region, and tail region. A bilaterally symmetrical animal can be divided down the middle into mirror-image halves. Humans have this type of symmetry.

Skeletons have one of two types (although not all animals have a skeleton):

exoskeleton Hard skeleton on the outside of body made of a stiff carbohydrate called **chitin**.

endoskeleton Skeleton on the inside of the body made of bones or cartilage.

Digestive systems

no digestive tract Individual cells digest and absorb nutrients from food.

incomplete digestive tract One opening for both food coming in and wastes going out. Digestion and nutrient absorption occurs in a single body cavity.

complete digestive tract Two openings, one for food coming in and another for removal of waste. This is the most specialized system—there are separate places for digestion and absorption.

2. Use the following dichotomous key to classify "unknown" animals into various phyla based on their symmetry, skeleton, and digestive system. After you have identified an animal's phylum, fill in the appropriate row in Table 11.7.

TABLE 11.7

Unknown Animal	Phylum
A.	
B.	
C.	
D.	
E.	
F.	
G.	
H.	
I.	

Key to Selected Phyla of the Kingdom Animalia

1a. Asymmetry . . . . .Phylum Porifera
1b. Radial or bilateral symmetry 2
2a. Radial symmetry 3
2b. Bilateral symmetry 4
3a. Incomplete digestive tract .Phylum Cnidaria
3b. Complete digestive tract . . . . .Phylum Echinodermata
4a. Flattened body with no appendages . . . . . .Phylum Platyhelminthes
4b. Other body types 5
5a. Long, wormlike body 6
5b. Other body types 7
6a. Unsegmented worms . . . . .Phylum Nematoda
6b. Segmented worms . . . . .Phylum Annelida
7a. Organism has a shell . . . . .Phylum Mollusca
7b. No shell 8
8a. Organism has hard exoskeleton . . . . .Phylum Arthropoda
8b. Organism has endoskeleton . . . . .Phylum Chordata

---

LAB EXERCISE 11.5

A Survey of the Kingdom Fungi

Fungi are heterotrophic, like animals, but the way they acquire their food is fundamentally different. Instead of ingesting their food, fungi excrete digestive enzymes and then absorb the predigested food through their cell walls, which are made of the protein **chitin**.

Fungi disperse via **spores**, which are single cells with tough outer walls. There are four different phyla of fungi, each distinguished by either a unique method of producing spores or a unique process of sexual reproduction. The classic toadstool-like mushrooms belong to one phylum of fungi, and only one other phylum produces large mushroom structures (although this phylum also encompasses bread yeast, which does not produce mushrooms at all). Mushrooms are only the spore-producing organs of the fungus. Most of the fungal body is made up of microscopic threads, called **hyphae**, which are found throughout the material the fungus is consuming. Other phyla of fungi include types of molds and mildews.

(20–30 Minutes)

A. Examine various specimens of the kingdom Fungi.

1. Examine under the microscope the slide of bread mold prepared by your laboratory instructor. Draw and identify the hyphae and the spore-forming structure.

Materials:
- *Light microscopes*
- *Dissecting microscopes*
- *Prepared slide of* **Rhizopus stolonifera**
- *Live and preserved mushrooms*
- *Prepared slide of* **Coprinus** *mushroom cap*
- *Samples of lichen*
- *Yeast and other economically important fungi (***Penicillium,*** blue cheese, corn smut/wheat rust/other crop pathogen) as interest and availability dictate*

2. Look at the live and dried mushrooms, as well as the slide of a mushroom cap. Sketch the mushroom cap here. Where are the spores found on this structure?

3. Yeasts differ from other fungi because they are not made up of hyphae, but are single-celled structures. Baker's yeast (*Saccharomyces cerevisiae* as well as other species of *Saccharomyces*) is one of the most economically important fungi because of its role in bread making (the carbon dioxide yeast give off as they consume the sugar in an unbaked loaf of bread causes the bread to rise), and in alcohol production (ethanol is a waste product of yeast metabolism in a low-oxygen environment). Examine the yeast and other economically important fungi available in lab.

4. Lichens are a symbiotic association of fungi and algae or photosynthetic bacteria in which each partner benefits from the other. The photosynthesizers receive a protected place to grow and access to water absorbed by the fungus and the fungus receives excess carbohydrates from the photosynthesizers. Observe examples of lichen available in lab.

5. Discuss the following questions and be prepared to share your answers with the lab instructor and your classmates.

   a. The hyphae of fungi are very diffuse and thread-like. Considering how a fungus acquires food from its environment, what advantages does this body form have over a more compact body form?

   Maximizes surface area over which nutrients can be absorbed

   b. Based on your observations of the bread mold, what do you think gives bread mold its "fuzzy" appearance?

   Masses of spores and aerial hyphae

   c. Some mushrooms are poisonous to humans and some are quite tasty. Considering that the "purpose" of a mushroom is to disperse spores, why might mushrooms have these different traits?

   One strategy for dispersing spores is to attract an animal disperser to eat the fungi and drop the spores as waste elsewhere; this would cause selection for traits that appeal to appropriate dispersers, including a pleasant taste to the "right disperser" and a bitter taste to the "wrong disperser." For other fungi, the spore dispersal strategy might require the mushroom to remain mostly intact; being highly poisonous would cause potential consumers to avoid these mushrooms, or to become ill and unable to eat many of them if they do try a sample.

   d. In what environments would you expect lichens to be successful and why?

   They can live on almost any surface, as the fungus stores moisture and the photosynthesizers make food from easily accessible ingredients. However, their generally flattened shape and slower growth rate means that they will be overgrown and overshaded by plants in environments with good soil and moisture.

B. Determine the requirements for fungal growth.

   You have probably had enough experience with moldy food to have formed some hypotheses about which environmental conditions favor or restrict the growth of mold. This exercise will allow you to test one or more of these hypotheses experimentally.

   Rhizopus stolonifera ("Black Bread Mold") is a common mold in the environment and one of the leading causes of food spoilage.

   1. What environmental conditions do you think favor the growth of mold? What conditions do you think restrict its growth? Be creative,

(15 Minutes Setup, 10 Minutes to Record Data in Next Lab Period)

Materials:
- *Petri dishes (2–4 per student)*
- *Bread - 1 slice per student (ideally, an organic brand, rather than one with preservatives)*
- *Culture of **Rhizopus stolonifera** on petri dish (1 for every 2 lab sections)*
- *Forceps for transferring small amounts of **R. stolonifera** from culture to bread*
- *Aluminum foil*
- *Paper towels*
- *Table sugar*
- *Table salt*
- *Other "additives" that might affect fungal growth (vinegar, lemon juice, and so on)*
- *Marking pens*

Instructors: Bread must be moist to facilitate mold growth. One option is to dampen the bread by spraying lightly with water before transferring the mold. If your lab environment is fairly dry, you may also need to seal the Petri dishes with Parafilm to avoid drying out.

and consider the variety of techniques we typically use in food storage to prevent spoilage. Record your ideas in Table 11.8.

TABLE 11.8

Conditions That Favor Mold Growth	Conditions That Restrict Mold Growth

2. Choose one environmental factor from each column and design a simple hypothesis test to evaluate your hypothesis. You will compare mold growth on a quarter-slice of bread that is exposed to the environmental factor in question to growth on a quarter-slice of bread that is protected from the same environmental factor. All bread will be inoculated with a small amount of *Rhizopus stolonifera*.

Hypothesis 1:
The following environmental factor - _____- favors the growth of mold.

Hypothesis 2:
The following environmental factor - _____ - restricts the growth of mold.

Prediction 1: If Hypothesis 1 is correct, I predict that mold growth on the treated bread will be _____ mold growth on the untreated bread after one week.

Prediction 2: If Hypothesis 2 is correct, I predict that mold growth on the treated bread will be _____ mold growth on the untreated bread after one week.

3. With the materials available in the lab, set up your hypothesis tests by applying the appropriate treatments and inoculating each bread slice with a small amount of *R. stolonifera* from the active culture in lab. Be sure to label your petri dishes with your name and the treatment you have applied. Briefly describe your treatments here. Petri dishes will be stored at room temperature for several days and then transferred to a cold place for the remainder of the week.

4. Record your results in Table 11.9. Indicate relative mold growth with the following scale:

   0 = no mold growth
   + = small amount of growth (<25% of bread surface)
   + + = moderate amount of growth (~50% of bread surface)
   + + + = bread surface completely covered with mold.

TABLE 11.9

Environmental Factor	Growth on Treated Bread	Growth on Untreated Bread

5. Did your results support your hypothesis? If not, why do you suppose they didn't?

   One complication is the fact that mold spores are so ubiquitous that sometimes other molds will grow on the bread. This result can be just as instructive as the "expected" result.

6. Did this exercise provide you with any practical information about protecting foods from spoilage? If so, what?

LAB EXERCISE 11.6

A Survey of the Kingdom Plantae

(20 Minutes to 1 Hour, Depending on Activities)

Materials:

A variety of plants of various phyla. If a greenhouse is available to you, a greenhouse tour can be an excellent way to survey diversity. Alternatively, a walk in a nearby natural area could fulfill the objectives of this exercise.

A. Survey the diversity of the plant kingdom.

The plant kingdom is divided into 10 phyla; of these, only four make up the majority of land plants. These four phyla can be arranged in a timeline that helps to illustrate the major advances in plant evolution.

Phylum Bryophyta – mosses Early land plants that produce spores for reproduction and do not contain vascular tissue, which in other plants transports water and nutrients throughout the plant body. These plants are thus necessarily small and close to the ground.

Phylum Pteridophyta – ferns and relatives Some species resemble early land plants as well. Produce spores for reproduction and contain vascular tissue.

Phylum Coniferophyta – nonflowering seed plants, including conifers Contain vascular tissue and produce seeds, which contain embryos encased in nutritive tissue and a seed coat produced by the parent plant tissue. Sperm is generally transferred inside of resistant pollen grains.

Phylum Anthophyta – flowering plants Contain vascular tissue, including cells that increase efficiency of water movement. Flowers lead to specificity in pollen transfer and result in the production of fruit, which serves as a dispersal mechanism for seeds.

1. Observe the various plant specimens available in the lab or in the field. As you examine the plants, try to determine which of the four major phyla each species belongs in (or which one it is closest to).

2. Based on your observations in lab and your previous knowledge, which of the four phyla do you think is most diverse? Which is least diverse? Which is most abundant? Which is least abundant?

   Anthophyta is both most diverse and most abundant. Coniferophyta is least diverse. Least abundant is not always clear—in most environments, Pteridophyta is probably least abundant.

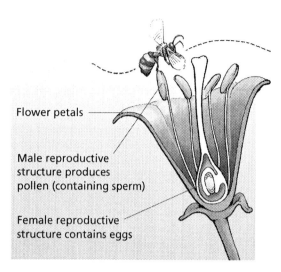

FIGURE 11.2

(20–30 Minutes)

Materials:
- *Large, easily dissected flower with easily seen parts. Any type of lily is excellent, although providing lilies for an entire class can be expensive. Fuschia is an easily propagated and adequate flower as well.*
- *A variety of fruits for dissection. Most should be simple, although it is instructive to throw in some interesting variations (for example, strawberries, pineapple).*
- *Scalpels, knives, and/or forceps for dissection*
- *Dissecting scope*

B. Dissect flowers and fruits.

People are often surprised to learn that many of the plants we consider "vegetables" are actually fruits from a botanical perspective. A fruit is essentially the mature female part (ovary) of a flower. Generally, fruits can be identified as such by the presence of seeds (although some of the fruits we eat have been artificially selected to be seedless, such as many varieties of oranges, bananas, and grapes). In this exercise, you will dissect a "typical" flower and relate the structures of the flower to various fruits.

1. Determine a flower's structure. Use Figure 11.2 as a guideline as you dissect the flower(s) available in lab. Try to identify all of the major parts labeled on the diagram on your flower.

2. Determine the relationship of flower to fruit. A fruit is most typically the ripened ovary of a flower, as described in Figure 11.3. Slice the ovary of the flower you are dissecting horizontally to observe the ovules inside. These structures develop into seeds as the ovary develops into a dispersal structure.

3. Dissect a fruit and identify seeds and other flower parts. Obtain a variety of fruits and examine them for the presence of seeds and any other structures that indicate their relationship to their source flower (for example, petals or stamens still attached). Be prepared to share your dissections with the rest of the class.

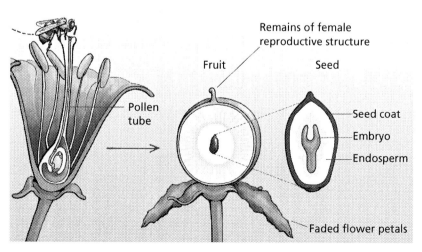

FIGURE 11.3

TOPIC 11
_____

POST-LABORATORY QUIZ

BIODIVERSITY

1. Describe the currently most accepted hypothesis of the evolutionary relationships among the three domains of life.

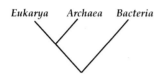

2. Most members of the domain Bacteria can be classified into one of two different types based on *cell wall structure.*

3. Name the four kingdoms within the domain Eukarya.
   Protista, Fungi, Plantae, Animalia

4. What physical characteristic unites all members of the domain Eukarya?
   Cells contain a membrane-bound nucleus, which envelops genetic information.

5. Protists are unique among eukaryotic kingdoms in that members of the kingdom do not share a single, typical, mode of nutrition. What characteristic appears to unite the members of this very diverse kingdom?
   All species have a single-celled, free-living stage at some point of their life cycle.

6. Describe the typical body form of a member of the kingdom Fungi and explain how this form relates to the fungus life style.
   Most fungi are primarily made up of thin strands called hyphae. These structures maximize the surface area of the fungus, which is an advantage for an organism that makes its living by absorbing nutrients directly from the material it is growing on.

7. The tough cells that fungi produce for dispersal are known as *spores.*

8. Describe two general characteristics that help define which phyla an animal species belongs to.
   Based on this lab, three possible answers: body symmetry, presence and type of skeleton, and digestive system structure.

9. For each pair, circle the trait that evolved first in the history of plant evolution.

   spores or seeds   *(spores)*

   seeds or fruits   *(seeds)*

   flowers or vascular tissue   *(vascular tissue)*

   photosynthesis or seeds   *(photosynthesis)*

10. Describe the relationship between flowers and fruits in flowering plants.
    A structure on the flower known as the ovary develops into all or part of the fruit. The ovules inside the ovary, after fertilization and development, become seeds.

TOPIC 12

Population and Ecosystem Ecology

Learning Objectives

1. Calculate the growth rate of a population from information about births, deaths, and current population numbers.

2. Define carrying capacity and explain how population growth rates change as a population approaches carrying capacity.

3. Define eutrophication and explain how it occurs.

4. Define biomagnification and explain how energy flow in ecosystems leads to this problem.

A pre-laboratory quiz is available in Appendix A on page 219.

Pre-laboratory Reading

The human population of Earth reached 6 billion in 1999 and it continues to increase at a rapid rate. At current rates of growth, the number of people on the planet will exceed 9 billion by the middle of the 21st century. The rapid increase in the human population is a relatively recent phenomenon, as shown in Figure 12.1.

Growth rates in any population are a function of **birth rates** (the number of offspring born per 1,000 members of the population in a given time period) minus **death rates** (the number of deaths per 1,000 members of the population in the same time period). Human populations have exploded in the past 200 years as a result of a dramatic decline in death rates as birth rates have remained stable or declined much more slowly. The result is shown in Figure 12.1—**exponential growth**, growth that occurs unchecked and in proportion to the total population number.

All other biological populations eventually run into some environmental limit that sets a ceiling on the number of individuals that can be sustained indefinitely in that environment. This ceiling is known as the environment's **carrying capacity**. The carrying capacity is a function of total food availability, increased rates of disease transmission in larger populations, limits on physical space for individuals, or the like. The growth rate of a population approaching environmental carrying capacity slows down as a result of increasing death rates and/or decreasing birth rates. The change in population

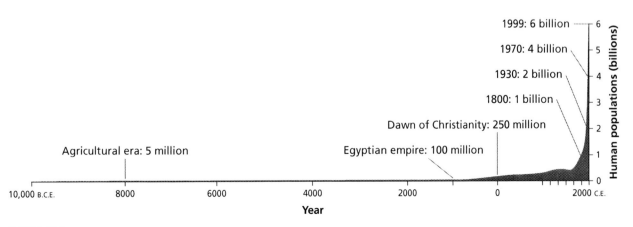

FIGURE 12.1

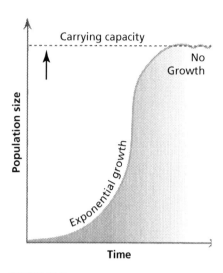

FIGURE 12.2

size over time in a population limited by the environment can be described by an S-shaped curve, as seen in Figure 12.2.

When a population is growing rapidly, it can often overshoot the carrying capacity of the environment. Most often, this type of overshoot is followed by a population "crash," resulting from very high death rates of individuals in an environment which has too few resources to support them.

Many people who are concerned about the rapid growth of the human population fear that humans are headed for a population crash, a rapid catastrophic decline in population size. Critics counter that the human population does not show any signs of approaching carrying capacity. For instance, death rates continue to decline, food is abundant, and measures of human health are for the most part improving. However, many of these gains result from the use of **nonrenewable resources**, primarily **fossil fuels**, which will eventually be used up. Whether the eventual result of the loss of these resources will be a crash of the human population is a matter of great debate.

We do know that the growing human population places strains on the natural environment. These strains are a natural outcome of the fact that human societies are enmeshed in the biological world. Many human impacts on the natural world occur to **ecosystems**—the interacting parts of the biological and physical worlds. The major processes that occur at the ecosystem level are the cycling of nutrients through organisms and the non-living world and the flow of energy from the sun (or another energy source) through a biological system. When human activities interrupt or change **nutrient cycles**, the effects can be major and devastating. One effect of a disrupted nutrient cycle is **eutrophication**, the modification of aquatic systems as a result of artificially high nutrient inputs. Energy flow in an ecosystem can also magnify human effects on the natural world. Because some energy is converted to heat at every transfer, animals that rely on other animals for food essentially ingest an enormous amount of the plants that their prey fed upon. Any persistent pollutants that are found in low levels in plants will be found in much higher levels in top predators, a process called **biomagnification**. As human populations continue to increase, our effects on ecosystems will only become more severe unless we understand, and adjust our activities to take into account, these ecological processes.

LAB EXERCISE 12.1

(55 Minutes)

Exploring Population Growth

A. Envision exponential growth.

(15 minutes)

The dramatic increase in number that occurs when growth is in proportion to population size can be difficult to conceive. This simple exercise will help you envision the power of exponential growth.

1. Obtain a piece of 8.5″ × 11″ notebook paper. The thickness of this paper (0.1 mm, or 1 ten-thousandth of a meter) represents the current population size.

2. Fold the paper in half—this represents a doubling of the population. In one generation, this would be equivalent to a growth rate of 100%. In a population growing at 2% per year (as in the human population), doubling requires about 35 years. The thickness of the folded sheet (0.2 mm) represents this new population size. Fill in the second row in Table 12.1, indicating the number of layers and the thickness.

Materials:
- *8.5″ × 11″ notebook paper, 1 sheet per student*
- *Calculators*
- *Graph paper (optional), 1 sheet per student*

TABLE 12.1

Fold Number	Number of Layers	Thickness of Sheaf	Comparative Sizes (Note: Supplied by Instructor)
0	1	0.1 mm	
1	2	0.2 mm	
2	4	0.4 mm	
3	8	0.8 mm	Thickness of fingernail
4	16	1.6 mm	
5	32	3.2 mm	
6	64	6.4 mm	
7	128	1.28 cm	Thickness of notebook
8	256	2.56 cm	
9	512	5.12 cm	
10	1024	10.24 cm	Width of hand
11	2048	20.48 cm	
12	4096	40.96 cm	Height of a lab stool
13	8192	81.92 cm	
14	16384	1.6 m	Average height of a person
15	32768	3.3 m	
16	65536	6.6 m	
17	131072	13.1 m	Height of a 2-story house
18	262144	26.2 m	
19	524288	52.4 m	
20	1048576	104.9 m	Height of a 25-story building

3. Fold the paper in half again. The population has doubled again. Fill in the third row in the table.

4. Continue to fold the paper in half. Most people can only fold the paper six or seven times. Continue to fill in the table.

5. Even though you are now at the physical limit of folding, continue to fill in the table until you have calculated the thickness of a piece of paper that has doubled 20 times.

6. Another way to visualize exponential growth in this exercise is to plot a graph of the change in the number of layers over the course of 20 foldings. Obtain a sheet of graph paper from your laboratory instructor. On the horizontal axis of the graph (the X axis), evenly distribute the numbers 1 to 20. Label the vertical (Y) axis of the graph in increments of 1,000 from 0 to 100,000. Plot the number of layers as a function of the fold number on this graph.

(20 Minutes)

Materials: Calculators, 1 per student group

The authors have used this exercise during lab periods as a class-wide project, where each student group does all of the calculations for a single country.

B. Calculate population growth rates.

Examine Table 12.2 and answer the following questions. Be prepared to share your answers with your lab instructor and classmates.

TABLE 12.2

Country	Births per 1,000 Population (as of July 2003)	Deaths per 1,000 Population (as of July 2003)	Population Size (as of July 2003)
Australia	12.6	7.3	19,731,984
Czech Republic	9.0	10.7	10,249,216
Norway	12.2	9.7	4,546,123
Panama	20.8	6.2	2,960,784
Tunisia	16.5	5.0	9,924,742
United States	14.1	8.4	290,342,554

1. The growth rate (symbolized by the letter r) of a population is generally determined by subtracting the death rate (d) from the birth rate (b) of that population, divided by the population size. In this case, because birth and death rates are calculated per 1,000 population (as shown in Table 12.2), we divide by 1,000. Symbolically, this can be written as:

$$r = (b - d)/1,000$$

Calculate the expected growth rate of the populations in each of the countries in Table 12.3.

TABLE 12.3

Country	Growth Rate
Australia	
Czech Republic	
Norway	
Panama	
Tunisia	
United States	

2. Given the growth rates calculated in question 1, calculate the number of individuals added to (or lost from) each population in 2004 (use

Table 12.4). To make this calculation, multiply the 2003 population by the growth rate. Symbolically:

change in population size $= rN$

TABLE 12.4

Country	Population Change
Australia	
Czech Republic	
Norway	
Panama	
Tunisia	
United States	

3. Given this rate of change, what was the population size of each country in 2004 (use Table 12.5)? Symbolically, this calculation can be written as:

$N_1 = N_0 +$ change in population size (calculated in question 2)

where N_1 equals the 2004 population and N_0 equals the 2003 population.

TABLE 12.5

Country	New Population
Australia	
Czech Republic	
Norway	
Panama	
Tunisia	
United States	

4. Use the formula in question 3 to estimate population size in these countries over the next 10 years. Fill in Table 12.6.

TABLE 12.6

Country	2004	2005	2006	2007	2008	2009	2010	2011	2012	2013
Australia										
Czech Republic										
Norway										
Panama										
Tunisia										
U.S.										

5. Review Table 12.6. Examine how the relationship among countries will change over the course of the 10 years. Note that developing countries have higher rates of growth. How is this important? Does

this information give you any ideas about strategies to reduce human population growth?

6. The growth rate of a given country actually includes more than just births and deaths—it also includes immigration to the country and emigration from the country. Most governments track this as an aggregate number called the migration rate (m), which is immigration minus emigration. The following formula summarizes the calculation:

$$r = (b - d + m)/1,000$$

How does the addition of this factor change *r* in these populations (use Table 12.7)?

TABLE 12.7

Country	Migration Rate	Growth Rate
Australia	4.05	
Czech Republic	0.97	
Norway	2.09	
Panama	0.97	
Tunisia	–0.6	
United States	3.52	

(20 Minutes)

Materials: Calculators, 1 per student group

C. Determine the effect of environmental carrying capacity on growth rate.

As a population approaches an environmental limit (that is, the carrying capacity of the environment), its growth rate drops. Ecologists have devised a mathematical formula that summarizes the effect of carrying capacity on growth rate, as follows:

$$\text{Change in population size} = r((K - N)/K) \times N$$

where *r* is the intrinsic rate of growth (that is, the rate of growth of the population when resources are essentially unlimited), *N* is the population size, and *K* is the maximum population that can be sustained by the environment. The growth rate at any given population size is estimated as:

$$r_{actual} = r_{intrinsic}((K - N)/K)$$

Use these equations for the following activities:

1. Given an $r_{intrinsic}$ of 1 and a K of 1,000, calculate the r_{actual} at the population sizes listed in Table 12.8.

TABLE 12.8

N	r_{actual}
10	
50	
100	
200	
500	
700	
900	
1,000	

2. Given an $r_{intrinsic}$ of 1 and a K of 1,000, calculate the population size in the generation immediately following generation N_0 in each row of Table 12.9. Recall that $N_1 = N_0 +$ change in population size.

TABLE 12.9

N_0	N_1
10	
50	
100	
200	
500	
700	
900	
1,000	

3. Describe why population growth rate declines as the population size approaches K in natural populations.

LAB EXERCISE 12.2

Eutrophication

Plant growth generally increases in response to the addition of fertilizer; in fact, this is why farmers add fertilizer to their crops and homeowners apply fertilizer to their lawns. It may come as a surprise, therefore, that fertilizer added to fresh water tends to "kill" these bodies of water. The process that results from fertilizer addition to water is known as **eutrophication**.

Eutrophication proceeds as follows: Fertilizer added to water increases the growth of aquatic plants, especially algae. Increased algae growth fuels an increase in the population of decomposers—particularly bacteria in the water. As bacterial activity increases, they begin using up the oxygen that is dissolved in the water to support their own metabolism. Oxygen levels in the water thus decline, and other aquatic organisms perish as oxygen levels reach very low levels. Waterways that have become eutrophic are generally coated with a greenish scum of algae and can experience die-offs of fish and other aquatic creatures.

Eutrophication is especially a problem in lakes that are in highly urbanized or agricultural surroundings. Communities in Minnesota that are concerned about the health of their lakes might have the option of monitoring the rate of eutrophication using remote sensing units deployed in their lakes. The Web site http://waterontheweb.org contains data collected from a number of lakes and rivers on oxygen levels and chlorophyll concentration (either measured as total chlorophyll or as turbidity, which is a measure of the cloudiness of the water) gathered by a remote sensor. This exercise uses these data to test one or more hypotheses about the factors influencing eutrophication.

A. Examine the descriptions of the lakes where data are being collected. Pay special attention to the descriptions of the surrounding land uses. Given

(40 Minutes, could be several-hour homework assignment)

Instructors: This is an open-ended activity that allows for a range of possible exercises. At its simplest, you can provide students with data from the following Web site and simply ask them to make a graph summarizing it and testing the hypothesis. Or, you can make this a homework assignment where students can gather data from the Web site and test one or more hypotheses.

Materials:

The actual information the students will use is dependent on the goals of the instructor.

- *Lake descriptions and data from the following Web site: http://waterontheweb.org/*

  Other organizations also are beginning to post real-time lake and river monitoring data for these types of educational uses. (One reviewer suggests The National Estuarine Research Reserve System database, available on the Web: http://cdmo.baruch.sc.edu/NERRMaps/NERRMap.cfm?set=1).

- *Graph paper for students or access to a computer with Excel or another data presentation program*

these uses, which lakes do you think are at highest risk of eutrophication? Which are at lowest risk?

B. Choose two lakes that you suspect have different risks of eutrophication to compare. Obtain the data for a single summer season for the lakes you will be comparing from the WOW Web site. The data relating to eutrophication includes chlorophyll concentration (listed as Chlor μg/L—not available for all lakes), turbidity (listed as Turb NTU), and dissolved oxygen (listed as dO, % sat). Graph the data (for example, dO at 7 meters from June to September) to compare the lakes over the course of a season.

C. Answer the following questions and be prepared to share your answers with your lab instructor and classmates:

1. Do the data support your initial hypothesis? If not, what pattern did you see?

2. How are chlorophyll concentration, turbidity, and dissolved oxygen related to each other?

   High levels of chlorophyll can cause high turbidity and contribute to low dissolved oxygen concentration at greater depths.

3. Given the results and the lake descriptions, can you make any suggestions to communities that are struggling with eutrophication in their lakes?

   Reduce use of fertilizer, plant forests or other natural vegetation around lakes, restore wetlands.

(20 Minutes)

LAB EXERCISE 12.3

Bioaccumulation and Biomagnification

Materials:
- *Hershey's Kisses, 1 bag per laboratory*
- *Calculators, 1 per student group*
- *Producers: 90% of class (in a class of 24– about 20 students)*
- *Primary Consumers: 9% of class (about 3 students)*
- *Secondary Consumers: 1% of class (1 student)*

Several of the inputs in modern agricultural practice are materials that are not found in nature. These inputs include insecticides, herbicides, and fungicides. Many of these chemicals are **persistent**, which means that they do not break down for long periods. Persistent chemicals can **bioaccumulate** (accumulate in biological tissues, such as fat) and **biomagnify** (become more concentrated in certain organisms).

This simple exercise will help demonstrate the process of bioaccumulation and biomagnification.

A. Your instructor will assign you to a particular category of organism. In this simulation, organisms are classified according to their **trophic level**—that is, according to what they eat. Producers are plants or plant-like organisms that perform photosynthesis. Primary consumers consume producers directly; these are also commonly known as herbivores. Secondary consumers consume primary consumers; these are commonly known as carnivores or predators.

Instructors will provide three Hershey's Kisses to each student—these represent the products of photosynthesis. You can have fun with this and use it as a review of photosynthesis—the producers can be theatrical in their "photosynthesizing."

B. Each producer will now begin photosynthesizing and producing sugar for its own use, as well as excess sugar that is available for primary consumers. These excess "packets" of sugar are symbolized by chocolate candies. As they are photosynthesizing, they are also bioaccumulating a persistent pollutant (symbolized by the candy wrapper) in their tissues.
Instruct the students to eat one Kiss and hang onto the wrapper.

C. Producers will use some of this sugar to support their own metabolism. However, even as they use the energy they have produced, they continue to store the persistent pollutant in their tissues.
Primary consumers should repossess the Kisses from a handful of the producers. In the case of a class of 24, each primary consumer should take the candy and the wrappers from 5 or 6 producers. Again, feel free to make this a game to keep the students' energy level high.

D. Along come the primary consumers. They will be eating the producers to obtain their "sugar packets" and will pick up the accumulated persistent pollutant as well (that is, all candy wrappers, including the empty ones).
Primary consumers should eat half of the Kisses they have and hang onto all of the wrappers.

E. Each primary consumer will use half of the remaining energy to support its own metabolism. Again, the persistent chemicals it has ingested will remain in its tissues.
Secondary consumers should take Kisses and wrappers from some (but not all) of the primary consumers, eat half of the Kisses (this may be too many for some students—of course, they shouldn't force-feed themselves), and retain all of the wrappers.

F. Finally, the secondary consumer(s) will eat. Each secondary consumer should obtain the "sugar packets" from primary consumers. While doing this, they will pick up any accumulated persistent pollutants. Each secondary consumer will use half of the energy gained to support its own metabolism, but will retain all of the persistent pollutant.

G. Calculate the average number of wrappers (both empty and containing candy) per individual in each trophic level and enter the data in Table 12.10. Draw a bar graph of these data, in which each bar represents the average number of wrappers in a given trophic level.

TABLE 12.10

Producers	Primary Consumers	Secondary Consumers

Average
number of
wrappers per
individual

Producers   Primary Consumers   Secondary Consumers

H. Answer the following questions and be prepared to share your answers with your lab instructor and classmates.

1. Describe in your own words why secondary consumers contain much higher concentrations of persistent pollutants than producers or primary consumers.

   As organisms at each trophic level consume members of the next-lower trophic level, they acquire both energy and persistent pollutants from their prey. Because a large percentage of what an individual eats is used by that individual simply to maintain itself, the pollutants become more concentrated in the tissues of each subsequent trophic level.

2. The pesticide DDT is a persistent chemical that was used widely in the United States from the 1940s until the 1970s. DDT was found in very high concentrations in birds that eat large fish, such as bald eagles and osprey. In fact, high levels of DDT in both of these bird species led to dramatic declines in their populations. However, DDT did not have such a dramatic effect on birds that eat small fish, such as common loons, or birds that eat aquatic plants, such as mallards, in the same environments. Use your understanding of biomagnification to explain why bald eagles and osprey were more affected by DDT than loons and mallards.

   Because bald eagles and osprey eat larger fish, and these fish tend to be older and have consumed many more prey fish than smaller fish, their bodies contain higher concentrations of persistent pollutants than smaller fish or producers. Thus, these birds received larger "doses" of DDT than loons or mallards.

3. Persistent pollutants also can accumulate in human tissues. One serious concern related to this fact is that breast milk fed to infants can have extremely high levels of these persistent compounds. Again, given your understanding of biomagnification, explain why infants who are breastfed consume higher concentrations of these chemicals than their mothers.

   Breastfeeding infants are essentially one trophic level higher than their mothers; in other words, the milk they consume is produced by a mother from her diet and from her stored fat AFTER she has used much of the energy for her own metabolism. Thus, while an infant consumes only a fraction of the calories its mother consumes, the infant receives essentially the same amount of persistent pollutants in those small meals that its mother received, in lower concentration, in her larger meals.

4. Although many persistent pesticides have been banned in the United States, some are still used as pesticides on crops grown in other countries and imported to the United States. Additionally, some persistent pollutants are produced in the United States as a result of the manufacture of pesticides (including pesticides whose use is banned here) and other products. Many of these pollutants have known negative health effects. Should the U.S. government ban the production, sale, and importation of these persistent pollutants, even if such a ban limits the pesticides available to farmers, or increases the costs of goods to consumers? Why or why not? What considerations influence your answer?

TOPIC 12
_____

POST-LABORATORY QUIZ

POPULATION AND ECOSYSTEM ECOLOGY

1. What has caused the dramatic increase in human population over the past 200 years?
   A dramatic decline in death rate, accompanied by a much slower and less dramatic decline in birth rate.

2. What is the growth rate of a population where the number of births per 1,000 population is 10.8, the number of deaths per 1,000 population is 7.2, and the migration rate per 1,000 is –2.4?
   .0012

3. What is the actual growth rate of a population of 900 individuals in an environment where the carrying capacity is 1,100 and the intrinsic growth rate is 1.4?
   .25

4. How do immigration and emigration change the overall growth rate of a population?
   Immigration increases growth rate, emigration decreases it.

5. Draw a graph of population growth that is restricted by an environmental limit over time. Label the horizontal axis "Time" and the vertical axis "Population size". Begin the graph with a very small population size, and label the segments where exponential growth is occurring and where the population has stabilized at carrying capacity.

6. What causes a decline in the growth rate of populations that are approaching the carrying capacity of the environment?
   As resources per individual in the environment become less abundant, the death rate of the population increases and/or the birth rate decreases because there is less energy or other resources to support individuals.

7. Describe why increasing the nutrient level in lakes can lead to fish kills.
   High levels of nutrients lead to an increase in algae growth. An increase in algae leads to an increase in decomposers when the algae die. Decomposers require oxygen to break down the algae, and their activities will drive down the levels of oxygen in the water, causing fish to suffocate.

8. Describe some environmental conditions where lake eutrophication is more likely to occur.

Surrounded by agricultural lands that receive high inputs of fertilizer.

Surrounded by urban/suburban environments with large amounts of lawn coverage.

9. Persistent toxic chemicals are found in highest concentrations in organisms at the highest trophic levels. Explain why this is the case.

At each trophic level, organisms consume both the energy AND the toxins contained by organisms at the next lowest trophic level. Thus, an individual at a high trophic level is consuming all of the toxins that were bioaccumulated by a very large number of low-level organisms.

10. Which chemical do you think is more likely to affect a large number of individuals as a result of biomagnification, and why?

a. Oxymyl, an extremely poisonous pesticide used to kill insects, which is water soluble and degrades within days or weeks in soil and water.

b. Polychlorinated biphenyls (PCBs), a group of chemicals that are extremely stable (do not break down under most conditions), fat-soluble, non-toxic in low doses, and were previously used widely in human construction as a fire retardant.

b. Problems with biomagnification occur with chemicals that are very stable and fat soluble, so that they remain in animal tissues for long periods and can build up in top predators. (Note: PCBs on the surface appear less toxic that non-persistent pesticides, but they are associated with cancer and reproductive failure and have been banned in the U.S. since 1977.)

TOPIC 13

Community Ecology and Conservation Biology

Learning Objectives

1. Identify species interactions as mutualism, predation, or competition.
2. Illustrate how changes in the interactions between and among species might directly affect humans.
3. Explain why genetic diversity within an individual can lead to increased fitness of that individual.
4. Define inbreeding depression.
5. Illustrate the process of genetic drift.

A pre-laboratory quiz is available in Appendix A on page 221.

Instructors: This lab does not include any living organisms (besides students). If you want to increase the "living organisms quotient" of this lab, you might want to include some of the ecologically oriented exercises from Topic 11: Biodiversity.

Pre-laboratory Reading

The focus of **conservation biology** is on the preservation and restoration of natural environments and habitats. Environmental conservation requires bridging the gaps between biology and sociology, environmentalism, law, public affairs, and economics, as well as many other fields of study. This is not an easy task, and often can be controversial. Amidst this controversy, the role of the conservation biologist is mostly to add expertise on the biology and sustainability of **ecosystems**, that is, the organisms in a particular area as well as non-living components of their environment.

A key to understanding ecosystems is an understanding of the science of **ecology**, the study of the interactions between organisms and their environment. In particular, ecologists seek to explain what controls the **distribution** (geographic extent) and **abundance** (total population) of species. A major component of a species' environment is other living species, and interactions among different species can take a number of forms that have differing effects on the ecosystem. When populations of two different species both benefit from each other's presence in a system, the relationship is termed a **mutualism**. The relationship between flowering plants and their pollinators falls into this category, as do relationships between cleaner fish and their "clients" and fungi and algae within lichens. Two species that use the same or similar sets of resources are said to be in **competition**; in this case, removing one of the two species would cause the remaining species to increase in population size. The interaction between agricultural crops and weeds is a competitive one, as are interactions between two species of large plant-eating animals on a savannah and those between algae growing on ocean-side rocks. When one species uses another as a food source, the interaction is termed **predation**, with the food source referred to as **prey** and the hunter as **predator**. Changes in the relationships among organisms can have profound effects on an ecosystem. For example, the loss of one species in a mutualism can cause the extinction of the other—this appears to be the case for a species of tree found on the island of Mauritius. The *Calvaria* tree has fruits containing very hard seeds. The seeds will not germinate unless their coats are heavily damaged, and the only way the seed coat becomes damaged is via passage through a large bird's grinding gullet (a digestive organ that functions somewhat like teeth). The only large bird native to Mauritius is the long-extinct Dodo bird. Thus, very few *Calvaria* trees are now found naturally on the island, and those that remain are ancient.

The decline in a population of a species affects not only interactions within an ecosystem, but also can affect the ability of that species to survive over the long term and to recover from the decline. Species that are **endangered** are typically those that have very small population sizes relative to their historical populations. For example, gray wolves were listed as endangered after their population size in the United States (excluding Alaska), which once numbered in the tens of thousands, declined to a few hundred after decades of hunting. These reduced populations face a number of threats. The most difficult of these threats to correct is the loss of genetic diversity caused by **genetic drift**.

Genetic drift refers to *random* changes in **allele frequency**; the frequency of, for instance, allele A1 is the proportion of A1 alleles for gene A in a population. The frequency of an allele can change simply by chance for several reasons—because some deaths occur by accident, or because some individuals with certain alleles happen not to reproduce. Genetic drift can cause large effects on allele frequency in small populations.

One reason that genetic drift is so troublesome is that it leads to a loss of **genetic diversity** in a population. Drift can cause the extinction of particular alleles from a population. Even if an allele currently has little effect on fitness, it might have an effect on the survival and reproduction of individuals under different environmental conditions.

In this lab, we will investigate the costs of species loss and endangerment to us and to the future of life.

(45 Minutes)

Instructors: If you would like a more sophisticated exercise, you might want to visit the following Web site: http://www.ecobeaker.com/ for information about an excellent set of computer simulations of ecological principles, such as the keystone species concept.

Materials:
- *20 red and 40 blue poker chips*
- *Caps, visors, or headbands—15 brown, 15 black, 8 gray (might need more)*
- *Large open area for "play" (at least 1,000 square feet)—flagging or some other method to set boundaries. The poker chips are scattered within the play area, but you should group red chips (aspen) together in "groves" and more evenly distribute the blue (grass) chips.*

Instructors: In a class of 24, begin with 6 elk, 5 beaver, and 2 wolves.

Note to instructors: "Elk" students will very likely have combinations of grass and aspen. If so, you might need to help them determine what their outcome is.

LAB EXERCISE 13.1

Keystone Species

In this exercise, you will take the role of a mammal in the Greater Yellowstone Ecosystem (GYE) to learn how interactions among species can have multiple and sometimes surprising effects on an ecosystem.

A. Your instructor will assign you to a role in the ecosystem game—either gray wolf (gray visors), elk (black visors), or beaver (brown visors).

B. The area designated by the flagging is the GYE. Notice that there are "food items" scattered about the ecosystem: red poker chips indicating aspen, blue chips indicating forage grass.

C. At your instructor's signal, begin foraging for food (and trying to avoid being eaten). Elk feed on both grass and aspen, and can collect both. Beaver feed on aspen only. Wolves feed on elk. Elk and beaver should collect appropriate tokens. Wolves should attempt to tag elk. An elk that is tagged must stop foraging and move off the ecosystem immediately (but should not lose the tokens). Continue foraging until all poker chips are collected or your instructor calls time.

D. Each participant should report the number of food items they consumed, and determine what that means for your next generation:
- Wolves: Consume 1 elk = survive

   Consume 2 elk = survive and have one healthy pup
   Consume 3 or more elk = survive and have two healthy pups
- Elk: Consume 1 aspen or 2 grass = survive

   Consume 2 or more aspen or 4 or more grass = survive and have one healthy offspring
- Beaver: Consume 1 aspen = survive

   Consume 2 or more aspen = survive and have one healthy offspring

E. If you have not consumed enough resources to survive, turn your visor over to your lab instructor. If you have consumed enough resources to reproduce, tell your lab instructor that you need a "baby." The lab instructor will identify one of the nonparticipants (either individuals who did not play in the first round or those who "died" in that round) as the baby and issue the appropriate visor. Elk and beaver should return the tokens to the playing field as your instructor directs.

F. Run this simulation four or five more times. Discuss the following questions:

   1. Is this ecosystem generally in balance? In other words, are all species of mammal surviving and able to reproduce?

   2. One characteristic often seen in predator/prey systems is a cycle where each species experiences regular "boom and bust" populations. Does that seem to be the case with elk and wolves in this ecosystem?

   3. How well do you think this simulation approaches reality? What factors are left out of the simulation that might also have an effect on these populations?

     Weather, other forms of predation, other reasons for mortality.

G. Now you will investigate the effects of removing a species from the GYE on our simulation. Gray wolves were exterminated from the GYE by the early twentieth century, and were only recently reintroduced (in 1995). To model the effects of this situation, you will play the same "game" minus any wolves. Play five or six rounds.

H. Discuss the following questions and be prepared to share your answers with your instructor and classmates:

   1. How did this simulation differ from the previous? Did any species become extinct or become very rare as a result of the loss of wolves? Did any become more common?

     Beaver and aspen decline, elk becomes more common.

   2. A keystone is a stone in an archway that helps maintain the shape of the arch. Without the keystone, the arch collapses. Use this definition to describe why wolves are a **keystone species** in the GYE.

     The whole nature of the ecosystem changes when the wolf is removed. Wolves had an effect even on species that they didn't seem connected to (for example, beavers).

   3. In the 80 years that gray wolves were missing from the GYE, elk populations increased, and aspen and beaver populations decreased. There were two reasons for this change: changes in the total number of elk and changes in the behavior of elk. Based on how food sources were found in this simulation (which is similar to how they are found in the GYE), what changes in elk behavior are beneficial to aspen?

     Elk tend to avoid bunching up in aspen groves because they are more vulnerable to wolf predation in these environments. (This might not work well in the game. Often it depends on how the "wolves" hunt.)

   4. Aspen groves provide homes for a number of species of warblers (small insect-eating song birds), whereas the wetlands produced by beaver activity provide homes for many other plants and animals that depend on these habitats to survive. Write the names of the "players" in this game, as well as the associated species described previously and draw arrows among them to illustrate the feeding connections among these species.

(This drawing, as well as the relationships among organisms, is called a **food web**.)

5. Using the figure you drew in question 4 above, identify species that are in competition with each other, those that are in predator/prey relationships, and those that are mutualists (at least in principle, even if their relationship is not direct).

   Beaver and elk are in competition; wolves and elk, beaver and aspen, elk and aspen, and elk and grass are predator-prey relationships; beaver and marsh-associated species and aspen and warblers are mutualistic (aspen benefit warblers by providing nest sites, warblers benefit aspen by consuming insect pests).

(15 Minutes)

LAB EXERCISE 13.2

Genetic Drift and Bottlenecks

Materials:
- *White and black "pony" beads (can also use beans, but it is important to ensure that different colored beans are approximately the same in size, shape, and weight), about 100 of each type per student pair*
- *Paper bags (lunch size) or some other opaque container (large envelopes), 1 per student pair*
- *Paper cups or 150-mL beakers for holding beads, 2 per student pair*
- *Calculators, 1 per student pair*

A **population bottleneck** occurs when a population goes through a rapid and dramatic decrease in size. (This is also called a population crash.) In this exercise, you will make and test predictions about the effect of a bottleneck on allele frequency.

A. Work in pairs for this exercise.

B. Obtain a paper bag, a cup of approximately 100 black beads, and a cup of approximately 100 white beads from the center table.

C. Your initial population consists of 100 individuals. The frequency of the "black" allele is 0.5 and the frequency of the "white" allele is 0.5.

D. To model this, place 100 black beads and 100 white beads in the paper bag. (Why do you use 200 total beans to symbolize a population of 100 individuals?)

   The protein coded for by the black or white allele has no influence on whether an individual will survive this resource limitation. In other words, right now, the gene is **neutral** with respect to fitness.

E. Imagine that the population in your bag lives in a wetland that is about to be drained for the development of a new housing subdivision. With fewer resources available, only a portion of the population will survive. In other words, the population is about to experience a bottleneck.

F. Predict how the allele frequency in this population will change in response to the bottleneck:

   1. Will the frequency of the black and white alleles both remain 0.5?

   2. Will a bottleneck that reduces the population to 30 individuals have a greater or lesser effect on allele frequencies than a bottleneck that reduces the population to 10 individuals?

G. To test your hypotheses, blindly draw 60 beads from the bag. The beads that are drawn represent the alleles of the 30 survivors of the crash. Count the number of each type of bead and record the data in Table 13.1.

TABLE 13.1

Population Crash to 30 Individuals	Black	White
Number of Beads		
Frequency (Number/60)		

H. Return the 60 beads to the bag and now draw 20 beads (blindly) to symbolize the crash to 10 individuals. Count the number of each type of bead and record the data in Table 13.2.

TABLE 13.2

Population Crash to 10 Individuals	Black	White
Number of Beads		
Frequency (Number/20)		

I. Discuss the following questions and be prepared to share your answers with your instructor and classmates.

Instructors: You might want to have students post their results on the board, to illustrate that there is no "pattern" to the drawing.

1. Was your first prediction correct? Was the frequency after the population crash different than the frequency before the crash?

2. Was your second prediction correct? If not, why not?

3. Did all groups have the same frequency of the black allele after the crash? Why not?

LAB EXERCISE 13.3

Drift in Small Populations

(40 Minutes)

A. Work in pairs for this exercise. You will pool your data with another pair of students.

B. Make hypotheses about the effect of population size and allele frequency on drift.

1. Is an allele more likely to become extinct due to drift in a small population of individuals or a large population of individuals? What is your prediction based on?

2. Is an allele more likely to become extinct if it is initially at a frequency of 0.5 or if it is at a frequency of 0.1?

C. To test these predictions, you and your team will run a series of four simulations of reproduction in a population. Each simulation will follow the same basic pattern, with slightly different numbers inserted at key points. One team should perform simulations I and IV, while the other should perform II and III. The numbers are provided in Table 13.3:

TABLE 13.3

	I. Large Population, Initial Frequency of 0.5	II. Large Population, Initial Frequency of 0.1	III. Small Population, Initial Frequency of 0.5	IV. Small Population, Initial Frequency of 0.1
In (A) spot	30	6	10	2
In (B) spot	30	54	10	18
In (C) spot	60	60	20	20
In (D) spot	30	30	10	10

1. Obtain a paper bag, a cup of 100 black beads, and a cup of 100 white beads. Place (A) black beads and (B) white beads in the paper bag. You will have a total of (C) beads in the bag. This represents the gene pool of the population, that is, the collection of all the alleles. You will now model the reproduction of this population over five generations.

2. When the adults in this population reproduce, they produce gametes (sperm or eggs) that carry their alleles. If 1/2 of the alleles in a population are black, 1/2 of the gametes produced by the population will carry the black allele. If only 1/10 of the alleles in a population are black, only 1/10 of the gametes produced by that population will carry black alleles. To model reproduction in this population, blindly draw (C) beads from the bag *with replacement*. What this means is that you should draw a bead, note its color (using hash marks on Table 13.4), and then return it to the bag before you draw the next one. We replace the beads because although there are only (D) adults (and thus (C) alleles) in the population, each adult can produce hundreds or thousands of gametes, so drawing a gamete containing a particular allele does not

TABLE 13.4

Generation 2	Simulation I	Simulation II	Simulation III	Simulation IV
Number of White Alleles				
Number of Black Alleles				
Frequency of Black Alleles				

reduce the likelihood of drawing a second gamete containing that allele.

3. Record your data in Table 13.4 for the simulation you are currently working on. The frequency here is the frequency of these alleles in generation 2 (the initial population of (C) beads represented generation 1). For simulations I and II, this frequency equals the total number of black beads drawn from the bag divided by 60. For simulations III and IV, it is the total of black beads drawn divided by 20. The frequency in generation 2 might be different from generation 1.

4. The numbers in Table 13.4 represent the offspring. This population has a unique allele frequency because it represents an assortment of alleles that were randomly drawn from the parental population. Therefore, to model continued reproduction, you must adjust the population of beads in the paper bag so that it contains the number of black and white beads listed on the table. You should still have 60 beads in the bag if you are working on simulation I or II, and 20 beads if you are working on III or IV.

5. Now you will repeat the drawing process with this new generation. After you calculate the allele frequency of the offspring, again adjust the numbers of black and white beads in the bag accordingly to model reproduction in the following generation shown in Table 13.5.

TABLE 13.5

Generation 3	Simulation I	Simulation II	Simulation III	Simulation IV
Number of White Alleles				
Number of Black Alleles				
Frequency of Black Alleles				

6. Continue this drawing and adjustment process for 2 more generations (Table 13.6 and Table 13.7).

7. Repeat steps 1–6 for the other simulation you were assigned.

TABLE 13.6

Generation 4	Simulation I	Simulation II	Simulation III	Simulation IV
Number of White Alleles				
Number of Black Alleles				
Frequency of Black Alleles				

TABLE 13.7

Generation 5	Simulation I	Simulation II	Simulation III	Simulation IV
Number of White Alleles				
Number of Black Alleles				
Frequency of Black Alleles				

D. Using a different pen color for each simulation, graph the changes in frequency of the black allele over time on the following chart. Label each line.

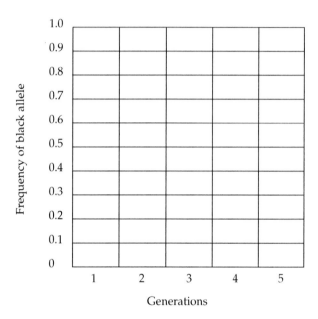

E. Discuss the following questions with your team and be prepared to share your answers with your instructor and classmates:

1. Were your predictions about the effect of population size correct? If not, why not?

2. Was your prediction about the effects of initial allele frequency correct? If not, why not?

3. Did the frequency of the allele change in a steady manner over time? In other words, did it generally increase or generally decrease over the period? Explain this pattern.

4. Did the black or white allele become extinct in any simulations? If not, do you think one would have been lost if we continued this simulation?

5. Consider what we can learn from this simulation about how genetic drift occurs in real populations. How does the initial frequency of an allele affect whether an allele is lost from the population? How does the size of a population affect whether an allele will be lost?

   Alleles in lower frequency are more likely to be lost than alleles in high frequency. Alleles in small populations are more likely to be lost than alleles in large populations.

6. Why is it a problem for an endangered species if their population remains small for many generations?

   They might lose genetic diversity in the form of alleles, with the consequences described in the pre-laboratory reading.

7. After a population has lost alleles due to genetic drift, is there any way to replace these alleles?

   Immigration of alleles from another population (that is, interbreeding with individuals from other population), mutation leading to appearance of new alleles.

LAB EXERCISE 13.4

Biocentrism Quiz

According to many conservation biologists, an important part of encouraging a conservation "ethic" among the nonbiologist public is conservation education. The most effective way that biologists can educate is to simply teach about and make easily accessible information about the natural world.

A. Assess your level of environmental awareness with the following quiz. Work alone. Your lab instructor will provide you with a key and grading guidelines.

1. How many days until the moon is full (plus or minus 2 days)?

   (+ 2 *if correct within two days*)

2. Name four native edible plants found in this area.

   (+ .5 *for each answer*)

3. From what direction do winter storms come in this area?

   (+ 2 *for correct direction [N, NE, E, SE, S, SW, W, NW]*)

4. Where does your garbage go?

   (+ 2 *for correct answer*)

5. Name or describe four trees that are native to this area.

   (+ .5 *for each tree*)

(20 Minutes)

Instructors will need to determine answers to this quiz for your own region.

Materials:
- *Calculators*
- *Overhead or chart on board with cells for writing in scores*

Note: You might want to supplement this exercise by leading a tour around the campus to look for native plants and animals, geological features, and so on.

6. What primary geological event/process influenced the land form in this area?

   (+ 2 for correct answer. Partial credit if students get one correct if several are important.)

7. Name two species that have become extinct in the state in the past 300 years.

   (+ 1 per species)

8. Were the stars visible last night?

   (+ 2)

9. What is the primary source of electrical energy for this area?

   (+ 2, partial credit if students get one if several are important)

10. Name four birds that are common in the area.

    (+ .5 for each correct answer)

B. Report your grade on the class chart. After everyone has reported a grade, calculate the average score and note the range.

   Average _____

   Highest Score _____

   Lowest Score_____

C. Discuss the following questions and be prepared to share your answers with your lab instructor and classmates.

   1. Did you think the quiz was easy or difficult? Did its level of difficulty surprise you?

   2. Consider the average score of the class. How do you think this compares with the average score of an "average citizen" of this region?

   3. How important is knowledge of the environment you live in? Are there any negative consequences of not knowing one or more of these basic facts about where you live? What are they?

TOPIC 13
_____

POST-LABORATORY QUIZ

COMMUNITY ECOLOGY AND CONSERVATION BIOLOGY

1. Describe the general effect of a keystone species on an ecosystem.

   Keystone species have effects that extend beyond their direct interactions with other species and that are crucial to maintaining the current structure of the ecosystem. When a keystone species is lost from an ecosystem, several other species might become extinct there as well.

2. Draw a diagram that illustrates the feeding connections (food web) described in the following paragraph:

   Kelp forests grow in the ocean waters immediately off the coasts of western North America. Within these giant stands of brown algae can be found a number of fish species that find shelter and food in the form of the larvae of other sea animals, including other fish, crabs, and sea stars. These smaller animals, in turn, live on smaller algae found in these forests. Sea urchins feed on kelp and can greatly reduce kelp numbers and height. Sea otters feed on sea urchins.

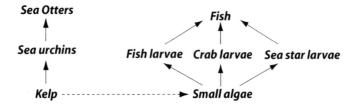

3. Use the preceding diagram to identify competitors, predator/prey pairs, and mutualists.

   Competitors: small fish, crabs, and sea stars (compete for smaller algae). Larger fish species (compete for animal larvae).

   Predator/prey: sea otter/sea urchin, sea urchin/kelp, large fish/animal larvae, animal larvae/small algae.

   Mutualists: none direct, but sea otters indirectly benefit kelp, kelp benefit large fish (although not clear how large fish benefit kelp), sea otters indirectly benefit all other animals in system.

4. Examine the diagram in question 2. What might happen to the ecosystem if sea otters are removed, as they once were when heavily trapped for their fur?

   Loss of sea otters leads to increase in sea urchins, leading to decline in kelp and kelp-associated species.

5. Why do population bottlenecks change allele frequency in a population?

   When taking a small sample of a larger population, it is likely that one will find that the sample is slightly unrepresentative of the larger population—sampling error (see Topic 1: The Scientific Method).

6. Review the following population descriptions. Is one more likely than the other to experience dramatic allele frequency changes as a result of genetic drift? Explain your answer.

A. Population of 50 individuals living on an isolated island

B. Population of 250 individuals living on an isolated island

Population A should experience more dramatic allele frequency changes, because it is smaller, and smaller populations show wider fluctuations in allele frequency as a result of sampling error.

7. Review the following populations. Is one more likely than the other to experience dramatic allele frequency changes as a result of genetic drift? Explain your answer.

A. Population of 200 individuals, 100 of them breeding

B. Population of 200 individuals, 10 of them breeding

Population B should experience more dramatic allele frequency changes, because it is effectively smaller, and smaller populations suffer more dramatically as a result of sampling error.

8. Review the following populations. Is one more likely than the other to experience dramatic allele frequency changes as a result of genetic drift? Explain your answer.

A. Population of 20 individuals, allele frequency A $= 0.9$, a $= 0.1$

B. Population of 20 individuals, allele frequency A $= 0.5$, a $= 0.5$

Both populations are the same size and should experience the same range of allele frequency changes. Population A might be more likely to lose allele A, but this does not reflect a difference in the magnitude of genetic drift in these populations.

9. Explain why alleles in low frequency in a population are more likely to become extinct due to genetic drift than alleles in higher frequency, even if the alleles have no current effect on fitness.

Sampling error is more likely to result in a rare allele being "missed" altogether. A more common allele is more likely to be picked up in a random sample of the population.

10. Describe the costs to individuals of low genetic diversity within a species.

Individuals in species where genetic diversity is low are more likely to be homozygous for a gene than individuals in species where genetic diversity is high. Homozygosity is a problem if deleterious alleles are present in a population—where heterozygotes might be able to "mask" the effects of these alleles with the actions of a nondeleterious allele, homozygotes cannot. In addition, heterozygotes might be able to perform over a wider range of conditions than homozygotes, because they can produce two slightly different proteins with advantages in different environments. In this case, homozygotes produce only one protein, so they might be successful over a narrower range of environments.

TOPIC 14

Gender Differences and Athleticism

Learning Objectives

1. Determine whether there are average muscle differences between males and females in your laboratory.
2. Determine whether there are average skeletal differences between males and females in your laboratory.
3. Test a hypothesis about sex differences in athleticism.

A pre-laboratory quiz is available in Appendix A on page 223.

Pre-laboratory Reading

At puberty, the gonads function as **endocrine organs** by secreting specific hormones. Estrogen is secreted by the ovaries of females and testosterone is secreted by the testes of males. Testosterone secreted by males leads to increased muscle mass. Some skeletal structures are larger in males to accommodate their larger muscles. Males also tend to be taller and have longer legs and arms than females because they begin puberty later than females. Because appendages grow at a rate that is proportional to the torso length, a later onset of puberty means the male torso will be longer when puberty begins, resulting in greater limb length. These differences lead to differences in female and male centers of gravity, with the female center of gravity being lower in the body.

The mandible, temporal bone, and frontal bone of the skull are larger in males to support their larger muscles. The pelvic bones also differ in females and males. Females have more broad pelvic bones (ossa coxae) and a larger, rounder pelvic inlet. The female pelvis is also flatter, more broad, and tipped more forward than the male pelvis, leading to a sharper angle between the hip and knee (the Q angle).

LAB EXERCISE 14.1

Gender Differences in Musculature

A. You will need to work in groups of three students for this exercise. One student will be the test subject, one will be the timer and one the counter. The test subject will curl the weight as rapidly as possible. The timer will call out "time" every 15 seconds for 5 minutes and the counter will record the number of contractions per 15 seconds below:

(30 Minutes)

Materials:
- *1 soup can or light dumbbell (1 pound) per lab group of three students*
- *Timers or clock*

Instructors: Try to have roughly equal numbers of males and females as test subjects.

Time Interval	Contractions	Same-Sex Class Average
0–15 sec	_____	_____
15–30 sec	_____	_____
30–45 sec	_____	_____
45–60 sec	_____	_____
60–75 sec	_____	_____
75–90 sec	_____	_____
90–105 sec	_____	_____
105–120 sec	_____	_____
120–135 sec	_____	_____
135–150 sec	_____	_____
150–165 sec	_____	_____

(Continued)

Time Interval	Contractions	Same-Sex Class Average
165–180 sec	_____	_____
180–195 sec	_____	_____
210–225 sec	_____	_____
225–240 sec	_____	_____
240–255 sec	_____	_____
255–270 sec	_____	_____
270–300 sec	_____	_____

B. Combine your data with the data from other same-sex test subjects in your laboratory.

C. Use a computer graphing program, or the space below, to make a line graph of the average number of contractions per 15-second interval (Y or vertical axis) versus time in 15-second intervals (X or horizontal axis).

D. Compare your graph to those of all different-sexed testers in your laboratory.

E. Based on this very small sample, does there seem to be a difference between the performance of males and females? If so, what is the difference?
   Males usually have more contractions overall and take longer to fatigue.

F. Can you think of some controls that would make this a better experiment?
   Compare males and females with equal amounts of training and fitness levels.

(30 Minutes)

LAB EXERCISE 14.2

Gender Differences in Skeletal Structure

Average sex differences in skeletal structure exist in humans. These sex differences include several differences in the skull, pelvis, Q angle, and center of gravity.

A. Determine sex differences in the human skull.

Materials:
Models of male and female skulls. A set including a typical male and female skull is available for purchase from Denoyer Geppert (part SK222) at a cost of approximately $210.00. If your institution has male and female human skeletons, the Q angle can also be demonstrated.

1. Compare the skull models from a human female and human male located on the display table. These skulls are labeled A and B. Which skull do you think is a model of a human male, and why?
   Some bones in the male skull are larger to accommodate larger facial muscles. These include the mandible (jaw bone), temporal bones (located at the temples) and the frontal bone (forehead).

B. Determine sex differences in the human pelvis.

Materials:
Models of male and female pelves. Pelves are available for purchase from many suppliers. We use Denoyer Geppert Science Company Part SV60 (male) and 215-61 (female) at a cost of about $60.00 each.

1. Find the two human pelvis models located on the display table. These pelves are labeled A and B. Which pelvis do you think is a model of a female pelvis and why?
   Female should have flatter, more broad ossa coxae and a larger, rounder pelvic inlet.

C. Determine sex differences in Q angle.

Materials:
Goniometer: These are available for purchase from Isokinetics Inc (1-866-263-0674) for about $10.00.

The Q angle is the angle formed between the hip bone, knee cap, and foot (Figure 14.1). To measure your Q angle, follow these steps:

1. Stand up and place your heels together as in Figure 14.1.
2. Place the rounded portion of the goniometer on your knee cap.
3. Point the upper portion of the goniometer through your femur toward your hip bone.

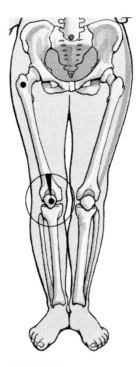

FIGURE 14.1

4. The lower portion of the goniometer should point along the line made by your tibia (shin bone).

5. What is your Q angle?

   The average male has a Q angle of around 13 degrees; females are around 18 degrees.

6. Why might males, on average, have smaller Q angles than females?

   The female's broader pelvis increases the angle.

D. Determine sex differences in center of gravity.

1. Weigh yourself on the provided scale and record the value below.

   Total Weight: _____

2. Zero the second scale at the end of the board, then lie down on the board with your head at the scale end and your feet at the book end. Record the weight below.

   Weight on Scale: _____

3. Use the tape measure and a partner to measure your total height in inches. Record the value below.

   Total Height: _____

4. Use the following ratio to determine the height from the floor to your center of gravity:

   Weight on scale ÷ total weight = height from floor to center of gravity ÷ total height

   Height from floor to center of gravity _____

5. To find your body's center of gravity, hold one end of the tape measure on your toes and measure up the number of inches calculated above.

6. Compare the average male center of gravity to the average female center of gravity. Why might a male and female of similar height have different centers of gravity?

   Different weights affect center of gravity as do shorter or longer legs as a percentage of total body height.

Materials:
- *2 bathroom-type scales*
- *1 long board (This board should be long enough for a student to lie on. The board should also be strong enough to support a student's weight without bending.)*
- *1 book that is the same height as the scales*
- *Tape measure*

Instructors:
Place the board on top of a scale at one end and a book at the other. The board should just cover the scale but allow you to read the weight. The book should be just under the person lying on the board and will have to be adjusted for different sized students. If students have concerns about being weighed in class, ask for volunteers and perform this exercise as a demonstration or try arranging mirrors above the scale that students can read while lying on the board.

(45 Minutes)

Materials:
- *3 indoor darts (rubber- or plastic-tipped) per lab group*
- *One ring structure sold with the dart set*

Suggestions:
- *Mark a line in masking tape 10 feet away from the ring. Also, place a masking tape square around the dart circle leaving about one foot of space between the edge of the circle and the square.*
- *On the blackboard or overhead have a place for students to log their points by sex. It is also possible to record the values in an Excel spreadsheet that also calculates means and 95% confidence intervals.*

LAB EXERCISE 14.3

Testing a Gender Differences Hypothesis

Sex differences in athleticism can be biological or cultural in origin. During this portion of the laboratory exercise, you will be measuring each student's ability to throw a yard dart accurately to determine if sex differences exist for this skill.

1. Devise a hypothesis about targeting ability in females and males.
2. Test your hypothesis as follows:

    This task involves the overhand throwing of darts into the circle. Standing with your toes on the tape line, each member of your lab group should throw three darts with his or her right hand and then three darts with his or her left hand. Award each thrower 2 points for landing in the dart circle, and 1 point for landing outside the dart circle but inside the tape square. Remove the dart after each throw so that landed darts do not obstruct other darts. Points are awarded for initial landing only. Darts carried into the square or circle by momentum are awarded 0 points. List your group member's scores here:

3. Write the scores for each group member, according to their sex, on the blackboard.
4. After the entire laboratory section has listed its scores on the blackboard, calculate the mean (average) for each sex by adding all the scores together and dividing by the number of participants in each group.

    Mean for females = _____

    Mean for males = _____

5. Using the data from the entire section, determine the range (lowest to highest score) of scores for each sex and whether the ranges overlap.

    Range for females = _____

    Range for males = _____

    Overlap of ranges = _____

6. Does the data gathered by the class support your hypothesis? Why or why not?

7. Would it be possible to predict the sex of an individual based on his or her targeting score? Why or why not?

    Probably not, due to overlap of ranges.

8. Are there sex differences in targeting performance between the females and males of this laboratory section? If so, why do you think these differences exist?

    Differences could be due to biological differences or due to differences in practice.

9. Skill at targeting would be developed by practicing many different sports. Find out if your lab mates have played sports that would help them develop this skill. Is there a difference in the amount of time one sex spent practicing this skill?

TOPIC 14
_____

POST-LABORATORY QUIZ

GENDER DIFFERENCES AND ATHLETICISM

1. Why do males, on average, have more muscle mass than females?
   Testosterone

2. Why does the male skull have some larger bones?
   To support larger muscles

3. What causes females to have a larger Q angle than males?
   The pelvis is tilted forward so that legs hang at an angle instead of straight down.

4. What factors need to be taken into account when determining center of gravity?
   Height, weight

5. Why is the female pelvic inlet more rounded?
   To birth a baby's head

6. How do overlapping ranges impact one's ability to make predictions about groups of people?
   Can't tell which group a person belongs to based on his or her score. They could be at the outer range for their sex or in the middle of the range for the opposite sex.

7. The ovaries and testes are organs in the _____ system.
   Endocrine

8. What bones differ between males and females?

   The two ossa coxae of the pelvis, and the mandible, temporal, and frontal bones of the skull.

9. On average, would you expect a male or a female to have a lower center of gravity?

   Female

10. For your lab section, did it appear that biological sex or amount of practice was the key determinant in targeting skill?

    Differs

Fertilization, Birth Control, and Sexually Transmitted Diseases

Learning Objectives

1. Understand fertilization and witness fertilization in a model organism.
2. Determine the biological mechanism of action for various birth control methods.
3. View several different shapes of bacteria and some examples of bacteria that cause sexually transmitted diseases.
4. See how disease can spread throughout a population.

A pre-laboratory quiz is available in Appendix A on page 225.

Pre-laboratory Reading

Human males produce sperm cells in their testes and females produce egg cells in their ovaries. Sperm and egg cells are both examples of **gametes**. Gametes carry one-half the number of chromosomes that other body cells carry. This decrease in chromosome number is accomplished when the process of meiosis occurs in the testes and ovaries.

Women undergo meiosis to produce egg cells. Typically, one egg cell per month leaves the ovary and is drawn into the oviduct. Sperm produced in the testes of males must travel out of the penis and through the vagina, cervix, and uterus of a female to reach the oviduct. If an egg cell has been ovulated and sperm are present in the oviduct, fertilization can occur. After fertilization, the egg cell rolls down the oviduct and implants in the lining of the uterus, where it begins to make copies of itself by undergoing the process of mitosis. The fertilized egg cell eventually gives rise to a multicellular organism.

Fertilization can be prevented by abstinence or by the use of different birth control methods. Some birth control methods, called barrier methods, prevent pregnancy by preventing sperm and egg contact. Other birth control methods kill sperm, thicken the woman's cervical mucus, or prevent ovulation. Surgery also can be performed to disrupt the ducts that sperm and egg travel through, permanently preventing fertilization.

Infectious diseases can be passed between partners during sexual intercourse. Disease-causing organisms include bacteria, viruses, protozoans, fungi, and insects. This laboratory will focus on sexually transmitted diseases caused by bacteria, protozoans, fungi, and insects because viruses are too small to view with the microscopes that are generally available in teaching laboratories.

Bacteria are single-celled prokaryotes. **Prokaryotes** have no nucleus or membrane-bound organelles. **Protozoans** are also single cells (usually), but they are **eukaryotes** and therefore have a nucleus and membrane-bound organelles. **Fungi** can be single cells or multicellular eukaryotes that resemble plants, but don't have chlorophyll. **Insects** are small animals without backbones (invertebrates). When any of these organisms cause disease, they are called **pathogens**.

Not all bacteria are pathogens. In fact, your body is the home to many beneficial bacteria. Pathogenic bacteria can cause several sexually transmitted diseases such as chlamydia, gonorrhea, and pelvic inflammatory disease.

Chlamydia is caused by the bacterium *Chlamydia trachomatis*. Symptoms of chlamydia can include pelvic pain and fluid discharge. Unfortunately, many people with chlamydia experience no symptoms at all and the infection goes untreated. Untreated chlamydia infection can lead to pelvic inflammatory disease and can result in infertility. Abstinence and condoms will prevent transmission of this disease.

(10–60 Minutes)

Materials:

- *Compound microscopes for each lab group*
- *Glass slides*
- *Fertile Sea Urchins: There are many companies that supply sea urchins. Marinus Scientific (714-901-9700) sells urchins at a cost of around $200.00 for urchins and shipping. Carolina Biological Supply sells sea urchins as part of a complete kit.*

  To ensure that there is at least one male and one female sea urchin, it is best to order approximately 10 sea urchins. It is difficult to determine the sex of sea urchins, so having 10 virtually guarantees that you will have at least one male and female. It is possible to save the gametes for several days. For large labs with sections that meet Monday–Friday, it is probably best to harvest gametes on Monday and again on Wednesday or Thursday. You should place your order a few weeks in advance so there is time to collect and ship them.
- *Dropper bottles of sea water for each group. Sea water can be purchased under the name Instant Ocean or can be made fresh using the recipe in Table 15.1. After mixing, adjust pH to 8.0.*

TABLE 15.1   Sea Water Recipe

Molar	Salt	G/Liter
0.425	Sodium chloride	24.6
0.009	Potassium chloride	0.67
0.0093	Calcium chloride * 2 H_2O	1.36
0.0255	Magnesium sulfate * 7 H_2O	6.29
0.023	Magnesium chloride * 6 H_2O	4.66
0.002	Sodium bicarbonate	0.18

- *0.5M potassium chloride solution (3.73g of KCl in 100ml of distilled water)*
- *One 5cc syringe*
- *Several plastic or glass Pasteur pipettes or eyedroppers*
- *One 5-mL microcentrifuge tube or test tube for sperm storage*
- *Beakers a little smaller in diameter than the diameter of female urchins*

See Appendix B, page 244, for additional suggestions.

Gonorrhea is caused by the bacterium *Neisseria gonorrhoeae*. Symptoms can include a thick discharge from the penis or vagina. However, many people, particularly women, experience no symptoms and this infection often goes untreated. Untreated gonorrhea can cause infertility in women if bacteria spread to the oviducts and cause pelvic inflammatory disease. Abstinence and condoms prevent transmission.

Pelvic Inflammatory Disease (PID) develops when an infection spreads to the uterus and oviducts. Symptoms, when present, include pelvic pain and difficulty becoming pregnant due to scarring and blockage of reproductive organs caused by the infection. Abstinence and condoms prevent transmission of pathogens that cause PID.

Bacterial infections can be treated with antibiotics, but these drugs might not kill all the bacteria present. Any bacterial cell with a preexisting resistance to the antibiotic will survive and reproduce rapidly because there is less competition from other bacteria. The resistant bacterial cells will pass on their resistance to their progeny, resulting in a large population of resistant bacteria.

Bacterial growth is exponential; that is, one cell gives rise to two, and those two yield four, the four divide to become eight cells, and so on. Exponential division results in rapid bacterial growth.

Many sexually transmitted diseases are transmitted by contact with fluids that carry the pathogen. Transmission can occur via contact with saliva, vaginal fluids, and semen. Other sexually transmitted diseases are transmitted by direct contact with the infectious organism, as is the case with trichomoniasis, pubic lice, and yeast infections.

Trichomoniasis is caused by the parasitic protozoan *Trichomonas vaginalis*. This disease is transmitted via sexual intercourse. The major symptom of trichomoniasis infection in women is vaginal itching with a frothy yellow-green vaginal discharge. Most men do not have symptoms, but some might experience irritation in their urethra after urination or ejaculation. Abstinence and condoms prevent transmission.

Pubic lice are transmitted through skin-to-skin contact or contact with an infected bed, towel, or clothing. The most common symptom of pubic lice infection, also called crabs, is itching of the pubic area. The itching is caused by an allergic reaction to the bite. This symptom starts about five days after the initial infection. Pubic lice are killed by washing the affected area with a delousing agent. Condoms will not prevent transmission of pubic lice.

Yeast infections are caused by fungi of the genus *Candida*. These yeast are normal inhabitants of the female reproductive tract. They increase in number when a woman is weakened by illness or upset by stress. Antibiotics, taken to treat bacterial infections, can kill vaginal bacteria and allow the yeast to grow, leading to yeast overgrowth. Yeast also can be passed from person to person, such as through sexual intercourse. Yeast infections are characterized by a thick whitish discharge from the vagina and vaginal itching. Men can carry the yeast in their urethra and pass the yeast on during sexual intercourse. Abstinence and condoms help prevent transmission.

An **epidemiologist** is a scientist who attempts to determine who is prone to a particular disease, where risk of the disease is highest, and when the disease is most likely to occur. Epidemiologists try to answer these questions by first determining the source of the infection.

LAB EXERCISE 15.1

Sea Urchin Fertilization

A. Fertilize sea urchins.

1. View the sea urchin egg under the microscope.

2. Add a drop of sperm to the egg while watching the egg cell under the microscope under low light. Fertilization occurs quickly. You can see

that fertilization has occurred when there is a halo around the egg. This halo is actually the fertilization membrane.

3. Turn off the microscope light so that you don't dry out the slide and check back every 10–15 minutes to see if the fertilized egg has begun to undergo cell division. This usually takes from 45–60 minutes for the first division to occur. If your egg cell begins to dry out, add a drop of seawater.

While you wait for your egg cell to divide, perform Lab Exercises 2–4.

LAB EXERCISE 15.2

Viewing Pathogens

A. Identify bacterial shapes.

Bacteria can be rod-shaped (bacilli), spherical (cocci), or spiral-shaped (spirochetes).

1. View the prepared slides of bacteria labeled A, B, and C under the microscopes. Which sample preparation shows cocci, spirals, and rods?

    A = _____

    B = _____

    C = _____

B. Identify bacteria that cause sexually transmitted diseases.

1. View the prepared slides of the bacteria that cause gonorrhea and chlamydia. Sketch these bacterial cells here.

2. Are these bacteria bacilli, cocci, or spirochetes?

C. Identify insect, protozoan, and fungal sexually transmitted diseases.

1. View the prepared slides of the insect that causes pubic lice (*Pediculus pubis*), the protozoan that causes trichomoniasis (*Trichomonas vaginalis*), and the fungus that causes yeast infections (*Candida albicans*).

2. Sketch these organisms here.

(20 Minutes)

Materials:
You will need the following prepared slides:
- **Rod, coccus, and spiral bacteria**
- **Neisseria** *and* **Chlamydia**
- **Pediculus pubis**
- **Trichomonas**
- **Candida albicans**

Instructors: Prepared slides are widely available for purchase. Companies that sell prepared slides include Wards, Carolina, and Triarch.

LAB EXERCISE 15.3

Birth Control Methods

A. Study birth control methods.

1. On the lab bench are various examples of birth control devices and pharmaceuticals.

    List the biological mechanism by which each of these methods prevents pregnancy.

    a. serves as a barrier to sperm and egg contact

    b. kills sperm

    c. progesterone causes thickened cervical mucus which prevents fertilization

    d. continuous doses of estrogen and progesterone prevent ovulation

    e. prevents uterus from supporting pregnancy

(30 Minutes)

Materials:
As many of the following as you can obtain: diaphragm, IUD, male and female condom, spermicide, cervical cap, diaphragm, Norplant, Depo-Provera, combination pill, and minipill. University Health Services may loan these items for class purposes.
a = diaphragm, female and male condoms, cervical cap
b = spermicide
c = Norplant, minipill, Depo-Provera
d = combination pill
e = IUD

(40 Minutes)

Materials:

- *One small test tube per group member. Number the test tubes. Each test tube should contain three mL of distilled water except one test tube per class, which should contain an acid solution. For multiple sections, prepare the acid solution by adding 2 drops of concentrated HCl into 150 mL of distilled water. These test tubes should be numbered.*
- *One eye dropper per student*
- *An overhead or blackboard table with as many columns as students in the class and five rows. The columns represent each student; the rows represent exchanges 1–4 and infection status. The students can record their data on the table for the entire class to view. When viewing the final results, it will be possible for students to work backward to narrow down the source of the infection to a few students.*

See Appendix B, page 245, for an example.

LAB EXERCISE 15.4

Disease Transmission

A. Determine how disease spreads in a population.

This exercise will demonstrate how disease can quickly be spread throughout a population and how epidemiologists try to track the source of a disease.

1. Locate the numbered test tubes on your lab table. Assign one test tube to each person at your lab table. The fluid in the test tube represents your bodily fluids. The bodily fluid in question depends on the disease that we're modeling. In the case of a cold, the fluid in the test tube would represent mucus and saliva. In the case of AIDS, the fluid in the test tube would represent blood and semen. Write the number from the test tube you were assigned on the following data sheet.

2. You will be using your test tube to exchange fluids with four other students. Each time you meet another person, you can exchange bodily fluids by giving them a dropper full of your fluids and taking a dropper of theirs. Gently swirl your test tube after every exchange. Record your swapping partner's tube number on the data chart. It is important that you keep track of the order in which you made your exchanges. Make sure that you mingle with all of your classmates, not just the other students at your table.

3. When you have finished exchanging, bring your test tube back to your lab table. You will now test your fluids for disease. Add 4–5 drops of phenol red to your test tube. If the contents of the tube turn pink, you have escaped infection. If they turn yellow, you have been infected. Record your infection status on the data sheet. Empty out the contents of the small test tube, and rinse both the test tube and eye dropper well.

Your Source Tube Number _____

Exchange #	Name of Partner	Partner's Source Tube Number
1		
2		
3		
4		

Were you infected? _____

4. Work with your lab table group to determine the source of infection in Part A. It is easiest to use the information in the format that is posted on the blackboard. You will at best be able to narrow down the possible sources to two, even though only one individual was infected to begin with. Who are the likeliest sources of your infection?

5. Only one person had the infection at the beginning of this exercise. After one exchange, two people were infected (the original carrier, and the person the carrier exchanged with). What is the total possible number of people infected by the end of four exchanges (that is, if an infected person always exchanges with a noninfected person)?

6. What term could be used to describe the rate at which the infection spread?
Exponential

7. Based on this understanding of infection spread, do you think it is more effective to concentrate money and effort on cures/treatments for infectious diseases or on slowing down or preventing the spread of an emerging disease? Why?

TOPIC 15

POST-LABORATORY QUIZ

FERTILIZATION, BIRTH CONTROL, AND SEXUALLY TRANSMITTED DISEASES

1. Describe the process of fertilization in humans.
   Gametes combine chromosomes and undergo mitosis. Occurs in oviduct.

2. List several barrier methods of birth control.
   Male and female condom, diaphragm, cervical cap

3. Which birth control methods also offer protection from sexually transmitted diseases?
   Condoms

4. How does the birth control pill prevent pregnancy?
   Prevents ovulation and hinders sperm travel through cervical mucus

5. Infection with PID causing gonorrhea and chlamydia often goes untreated. If a woman has an untreated infection that advances to PID, why can't antibiotic treatment necessarily prevent her from becoming infertile?
   She may have damage to her oviducts that blocks or scars them, which interferes with fertilization.

6. How do yeast infections arise?
   Antibiotics can kill normal bacterial flora allowing yeast to propagate, stress can change the environment to favor yeast reproduction, or yeast can be passed from a man to a woman during intercourse.

7. Can men transmit yeast infections to women?
   Yes, if the man is infected, he is contagious.

8. Why does having pubic lice make the pubic area itchy?

   Allergic reaction to being bitten by lice

9. If a person did not exchange fluids from their test tube during Lab Exercise 15.4, is there any chance he or she could become infected?

   No

10. Is it always possible to determine who the first person to transmit an infectious disease was?

    No

TOPIC 16

The Human Nervous System

Learning Objectives

1. Describe the transmission of a nerve impulse.
2. Describe how psychoactive drugs affect the nervous system.
3. Understand the functions of the general senses.
4. Delineate the difference between a reflex and an integrated response to a stimulus.
5. Apply the scientific method to questions about senses and learning.

A pre-laboratory quiz is available in Appendix A on page 227.

Pre-laboratory Reading

Every second, millions of signals are generated by stimuli that help regulate your body's movements and environment. Your **nervous system** (see Figure 16.1) interprets these messages and decides how to respond. Interpreting and responding to stimuli requires the action of specialized cells called **neurons** (see Figure 16.2). These cells are often bundled together, producing structures called **nerves**. The nervous system consists of the brain, the spinal cord, the sense organs, and the nerves that link these organs together.

Information about your body's movements and environment—sensory input—is detected by **sensory receptors**. When the neurons of these receptors are stimulated, signals are generated and carried to the brain for decoding and integration with other information. Our senses consist of five **general senses** and five **special senses**. The general senses, receptors for which are scattered around the body, are temperature, touch, pain, pressure, and body position. The special senses, receptors for which are found in specialized **sense organs**, are smell, taste, hearing, vision, and equilibrium.

Although the brain is the primary organ of sensory integration, some responses to stimuli do not require its involvement. These responses are called

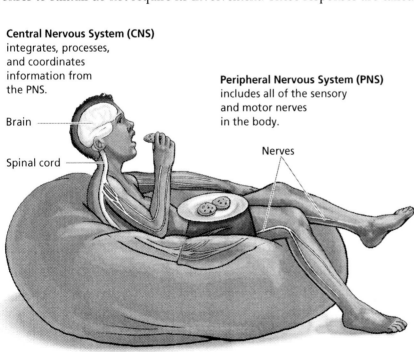

Central Nervous System (CNS) integrates, processes, and coordinates information from the PNS.

Brain

Spinal cord

Peripheral Nervous System (PNS) includes all of the sensory and motor nerves in the body.

Nerves

FIGURE 16.1

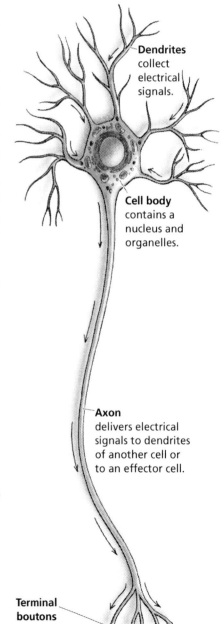

Dendrites collect electrical signals.

Cell body contains a nucleus and organelles.

Axon delivers electrical signals to dendrites of another cell or to an effector cell.

Terminal boutons

FIGURE 16.2

reflexes and are "prewired" in a circuit of neurons called a reflex arc, consisting of a **sensory neuron** that receives information from a sensory receptor, an **interneuron** that passes the information along, and a **motor neuron** that causes a muscle response. Reflexes cause you to react quickly to dangerous stimuli; for instance, the withdrawal reflex occurs when you touch something hot.

To carry information between parts of the body, the cells of the nervous system pass electrical and chemical signals to each other. Information is carried along nerves by electrical charges called **nerve impulses**. Nerve impulses

(a) Resting nerve cell

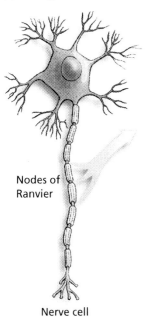

Nodes of Ranvier

Nerve cell

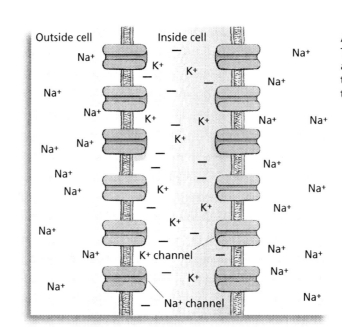

All channels are closed. The inside of the cell has a more negative charge than the outside of the cell.

(b) Propagation of an action potential or nerve impulse

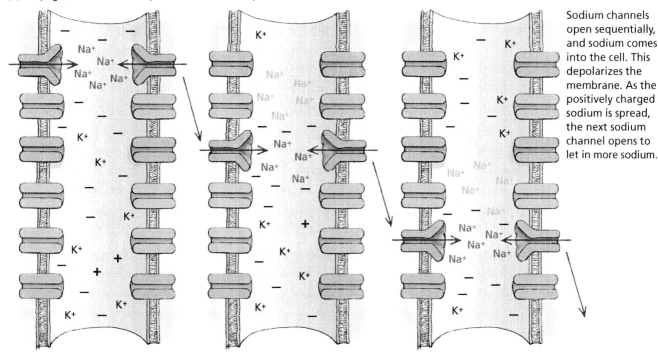

Sodium channels open sequentially, and sodium comes into the cell. This depolarizes the membrane. As the positively charged sodium is spread, the next sodium channel opens to let in more sodium.

FIGURE 16.3

are transmitted between neurons and from neurons to other cells by chemical stimuli, called **neurotransmitters**, released from the neurons.

A nerve impulse results from a small electrical change that is conducted along the length of a neuron. The inside of a neuron is negatively charged relative to the outside as a result of a difference in the concentration of positively charged sodium ions inside and outside of the cell. When a neuron is stimulated, sodium channels open and positively charged ions flow into the cell. A domino effect known as an **action potential** occurs as the positively charged sodium ions move toward neighboring sodium channels, causing them to open and let in additional sodium. The sodium ions also attract other, negatively charged ions from elsewhere in the cell; this effectively neutralizes the positive charge at the original site of the stimulus, causing the sodium channels to close. In this way, a nerve impulse is transmitted in one direction along the length of the axon of a neuron (see Figure 16.3).

Adjacent neurons are not directly attached to each other; they are separated by small gaps called **synapses**. When a nerve impulse reaches the end of a neuron, neurotransmitters are released that chemically conduct the impulse across the synapse. Neurotransmitters released by one cell bind to specialized cell receptors on the membrane of an adjacent cell (see Figure 16.4). This binding stimulates a change in the uptake of sodium, and thus triggers an action potential in the receptive cell.

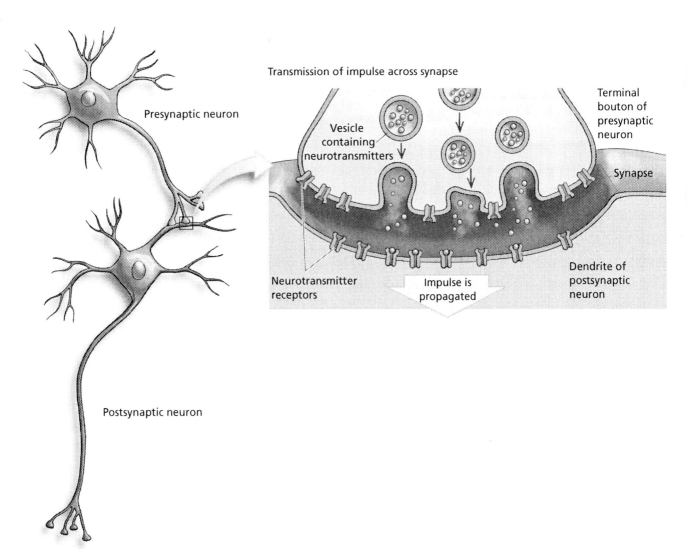

FIGURE 16.4

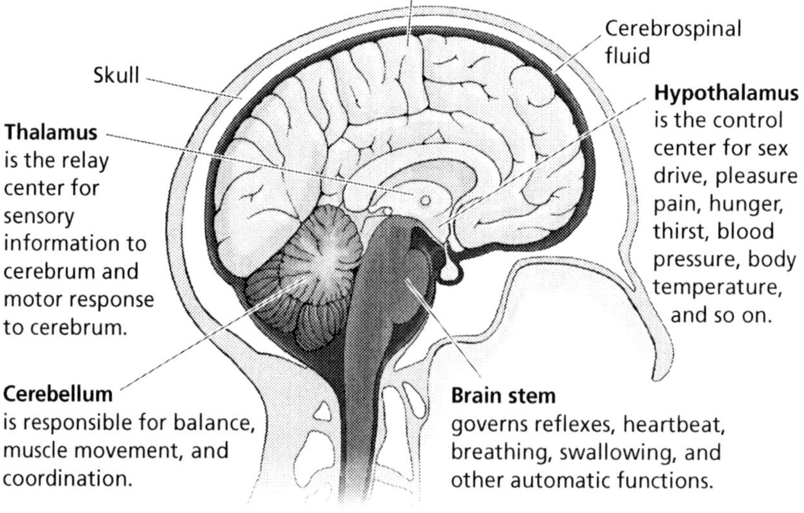

Cerebrum
controls language, memory, sensations, and decision making.

Skull

Thalamus
is the relay
center for
sensory
information to
cerebrum and
motor response
to cerebrum.

Cerebrospinal
fluid

Hypothalamus
is the control
center for sex
drive, pleasure
pain, hunger,
thirst, blood
pressure, body
temperature,
and so on.

Cerebellum
is responsible for balance,
muscle movement, and
coordination.

Brain stem
governs reflexes, heartbeat,
breathing, swallowing, and
other automatic functions.

FIGURE 16.5

After the neurotransmitter evokes a response, it is removed from the synapse. Enzymes degrade some neurotransmitters, while others are reabsorbed by the neuron that secreted them, a process called **reuptake**. The rapid removal of neurotransmitters from a synapse prevents continued stimulation of a nerve.

Neurotransmitters play an important role in coordinating the responses of the brain to outside stimuli. The brain is organized into three major regions: the cerebrum, the cerebellum, and the brain stem, each with a different role in processing and controlling bodily functions (see Figure 16.5). Many **psychoactive** drugs are either mimics of brain-specific neurotransmitters or affect the release, degradation, or reuptake of these neurotransmitters. By affecting the activities of neurons in the brain, psychoactive drugs have the ability to change an individual's feelings, perception, and ability to integrate and respond to stimuli. For example, cocaine decreases the reuptake of the neurotransmitters norepinephrine and dopamine, leading to a rush of intense pleasure (a result of increased dopamine activity), and increased physical vigor (a result of increased norepinephrine activity).

(15 Minutes)

LAB EXERCISE 16.1

Model Transmission of Nerve Impulses Within and Between Neurons

Materials:
- *2-inch diameter lightweight balls (5 per student group)*
- *Stopwatch (1 per student group)*

Instructors: A suggested role play—students line up with hands outstretched to sides, holding hands. The last student in the line (leftmost) holds the balls in his or her left hand. The students' arms represent unmyelinated sections of the axon; their bodies are myelinated sections. Transmission of impulse can be symbol-

The axon of a neuron is "insulated" with a material called the myelin sheath, made up of Schwann cells (see Figure 16.6). When a nerve impulse travels along an axon, the electrical signal jumps the gap between adjacent cells in the sheath.

A. Work with five other students to role play conduction along a single neuron. The end result of the transmission of an impulse from one end of the neuron to the other is the release of a neurotransmitter, symbolized by the balls. Use your imagination and creativity! Consider how you might demonstrate the propagation of a nerve impulse on the unmyelinated sections of an axon (review Figure 16.3), and how you might symbolize the

Nerve impulses travel more quickly on myelinated than on unmyelinated nerves.

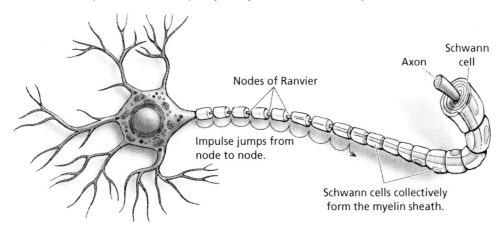

FIGURE 16.6

intervening myelinated sections. Share your role play with your lab instructor and the other students in the class.

B. Determine the length of time required for a nerve impulse to travel along your "neuron."

1. Measure the total length of the axon as you and your teammates are modeling it.

= _____ meters

2. Time from initial nerve impulse until release of neurotransmitter

= _____ seconds

3. Determine the rate of transmission by dividing the length by the time.

= _____ meters/second

C. Now you and your teammates should role-play the transmission of nerve impulses among neurons via the use of neurotransmitters. Remember that neurotransmitters do not remain in the synapse for long and are either degraded or taken up again by the neuron that released them. In this role play, each individual is a single neuron—the balls still symbolize neurotransmitters. Share your role play with your lab instructors and other students.

D. Discuss the following questions and be prepared to share your answers with your lab instructor and classmates:

1. How did the fastest rate of transmission your teammates generated in the first role play compare to the fastest neurons, which transmit at 200 meters/second?

2. Not all neurons respond to the same neurotransmitters. How could you have modeled this in your second role play?

ized (very simply) as a "wave" that transmits from one student's left arm to the adjacent student's right arm, across his or her body instantaneously and then along that student's left arm to the right arm of the next student. When the impulse reaches the "end" of the axon, the last student releases the balls (neurotransmitters). Your students may come up with creative variations of this idea, which is the most common one the authors have seen.

Each neuron should have its own "neurotransmitters"—picking up a neurotransmitter from a neighboring "neuron" will start an action potential in a neuron, which traverses from one "end" of the neuron to another (for example, from hand to legs or from one hand across the body to the other hand), causing the release of the neuron's own transmitters.

LAB EXERCISE 16.2   *(20 Minutes)*

Discuss Human Modifications of Neurotransmission

A. Discuss the following questions at your lab table and be prepared to share your answers with your lab instructor and other students in the class:

1. Some psychoactive drugs are illegal, such as cocaine and heroin; others are legal, but only obtained via a doctor's prescription, such as Ritalin

and Prozac; and still others are legal and available over the counter, such as nicotine. Do you think there should be a set standard for characteristics of psychoactive drugs that can be legally obtained and those that should be illegal (for example, degree of brain function modification, side effects, risk of addiction)?

2. Many experts on drug addiction call this condition a "brain disease." Repeated drug use actually changes the brain—changes ranging from fundamental and long-lasting changes in the biochemical makeup of the brain, to mood changes, to changes in memory processes and motor skills. These changes have a tremendous impact on all aspects of a person's behavior. For instance, drugs that stimulate neurons in the brain's "pleasure centers" actually dull these neurons to normal levels of "pleasure" neurotransmitters and make the user less able to appreciate normal positive life events. Does the fact that drug use changes the structure of the brain, leading to addiction, affect your feelings about the safety of the recreational use of addictive drugs? Does it affect your feelings about those who are addicted? Explain your answer.

3. Attention Deficit Disorder (ADD) and chronic depression are also often considered brain diseases. These two conditions are commonly treated with psychoactive drugs. Some critics of drug therapy for these conditions argue that we are drugging people for being human and that our society's acceptance of depression and ADD as illnesses is in stark contrast to the general feeling that addiction to illegal drugs is a problem of personal responsibility, when the science shows that they are essentially two sides of the same coin. Do you agree with these critics? How else might we, as a society, deal with ADD and depression?

LAB EXERCISE 16.3

Investigating the General Senses

A. Study reflex reactions.

Most reflex arcs are associated with sensory neurons that transmit pain or body position signals. One commonly tested reflex arc is known as the patellar reflex, which normally is triggered as you begin to lose your balance from an upright position. When you stand, the patellar tendon in your knee is carrying the load of your weight. As you begin to fall, this tendon becomes slack, which triggers the reflex causing your quadriceps (thigh) muscle to contract rapidly, launching your body up in the air. The little hop that results gives your body time to get your feet back under you.

Your patellar reflex may be tested in the course of a physical; any oddities in the reflex might signal neurological trouble.

In this exercise, you will use the rubber hammer available to test the patellar reflex of your lab partner.

1. The subject should sit on the lab bench with legs hanging (not touching the floor). Alternatively, the subject may cross his or her legs so that one is elevated. If you want to measure the reflex response, have another student hold a meter stick perpendicular to your subject's ankle.

2. Locate the patella on the front of your subject's knee, between the bony points of the kneecap and the top of the shinbone.

3. Using the narrower point of the reflex hammer head, tap your partner's patellar tendon firmly.

B. Test sensitivity to touch.

Receptors for touch are not evenly distributed on the surface of the skin. You can observe this with a simple "two-point test." In this test, the

---

(Time varies depending on whether hypothesis tests are performed; can be set up as "stations" for groups of students to rotate through.)

Instructors: Two of these exercises require students to touch each other (A and B) and one (C) asks them to expose themselves to a certain amount of pain. The authors urge you to use your best judgment when determining whether these activities are appropriate in your class situation. We have found that using the "stations" approach and making clear beforehand that students are not required to participate, but can simply watch others if they are uncomfortable, has been an effective way to maintain the comfort level of most students. In the smaller groups and somewhat noisier "station" set up, they feel less inhibited and less stigmatized if they still do not want to participate. Instructors should closely monitor activities, especially at these stations, to help maintain a nonthreatening environment as well.

(10 minutes without hypothesis test)

Materials:
- *Reflex hammer*
- *Meter stick (optional)*

Instructors: the patellar reflex is even simpler than the "typical" reflex described in the lab introduction: in it, the sensory neuron is connected directly to the motor neuron with no intervening interneuron.

It is possible to modify this simple exercise into a hypothesis test. Students might want to examine whether there is a difference in reflex response when the trigger is expected (that is, they are watching the test) or unexpected, whether the response diminishes over the course of several tests, or whether there is an effect of age, weight, or gender on responsiveness.

subject is touched on various parts of the body by two points simultaneously; the distance between the points at which the subject can distinguish two separate points is a rough measure of the density of touch receptors.

1. Examine the list of body parts in Table 16.1 and rate them according to the density of touch receptors you expect to find.
2. Perform the two-point test on your subject as follows:

    a. Modify a paper clip into a U-shape with equal legs. Wipe the points of the clip with an alcohol-moistened cotton ball to disinfect them. Initially, the distance between the points should be about 1 centimeter.

    b. Your subject should have his or her eyes closed or should be looking away as you perform the test.

    c. For each region of the body listed in Table 16.1, touch the subject's skin lightly with both points of the paper clip. Ask the subjects if they feel one point or two touching their skin. Pick up the points, move them closer together and gently touch the skin of the same area again. The points on the paper clip should be moved closer together until the test subject can no longer distinguish two separate points. You can randomly test the reliability of your subject's responses by touching with only one point occasionally. If they still report two points, you know that they are not a reliable subject for the test.

TABLE 16.1

Body Part	Rating (High, Medium, or Low Number of Receptors)
Forehead	
Cheek	
Lips	
Tongue	
Back of neck	
Back of forearm	
Palm	
Tip of Index finger	
Tip of thumb	

    d. Measure the distance between the points after the subject can no longer distinguish two points, and determine the approximate density of touch receptors by taking the reciprocal of this distance. The reciprocal can be calculated by dividing the measurements into 1. If the two-point discrimination on the cheek is 2.0 mm, the reciprocal would be 0.5. Fill in Table 16.2.

3. How accurate were your predictions of density of touch receptors?
4. Compare and contrast two areas that differ in their density of touch receptors. Why do you think there is a difference in sensitivity? Is this a difference individuals are born with, or do you think insensitivity to touch can be learned?

C. Determine pain perception.

Sensitivity to pain differs markedly among individuals for unknown reasons. Some percentage of these differences is systematic; in other words, certain age groups have higher sensitivity and there are differences in sensitivity between genders.

(20 minutes without additional hypothesis test)

Materials:
- *Large paper clips*
- *Alcohol and cotton balls to disinfect points between subjects*
- *Rulers*

Instructors: This also can be modified into a more involved hypothesis test—one possibility is examining whether there is a difference in touch sensitivity between genders.

(10 minutes per student group; 15 minutes to synthesize, summarize, and discuss whole class data)

Materials:
- *Ice water bath*
- *Stop watch*
- *Towels*

Instructors: Keep the ice water bath icy! Also, if your students are competitive, it is a good idea to limit the amount of time they can leave their hand in the ice bath so they don't get frostbite.

TABLE 16.2

Body Part	Maximum Distance Between Points Where Discrimination Impossible	Reciprocal
Forehead		
Cheek		
Lips		
Tongue		
Back of neck		
Back of forearm		
Palm		
Tip of index finger		
Tip of thumb		

A simple way to measure pain sensitivity is the cold pressor test: the number of seconds an individual is able to keep his or her hand completely submerged in an ice-cold water bath is a measure of pain tolerance.

1. Make a hypothesis about differences between genders in pain tolerance. Which gender do you expect to be more tolerant of pain than the other? Be prepared to defend your answer.
2. Make a general prediction about the average results of the cold pressor test for each gender, given your hypothesis.
3. Collect data on cold tolerance among men and women in your class (or recruited from elsewhere) and fill in Table 16.3.

TABLE 16.3   Number of Seconds Hand Submerged in Ice Water Bath

Men	Women

Average number of seconds: men _____   women _____

4. Did the results conform to your prediction? Did you support or reject your hypothesis? What further tests might be needed?

5. Were you surprised by the results? Discuss an explanation for them.

   Women are typically more tolerant of pain than men; although in class, the measured difference might be small or non-existent. One common explanation related to the theory of natural selection is that because humans experience difficult birthing, women who had lower sensitivity to pain tended to survive birthing and have more children overall than women with high sensitivity.

D. Study body position.

   The general sense that is perhaps most difficult to appreciate is proprioception—the perception of body position. This sense enables us to move effectively in our environment. To demonstrate this "muscle sense," perform the following exercise with a partner.

(15 minutes)

Materials:
- *500-mL beakers (2 per student group)*
- *Wax pencil*
- *Blindfold*
- *100-mL graduated cylinder*

1. Work in pairs for this exercise.
2. Take two 500-mL beakers, label one A and the other B, and fill both with 250 mL water.
3. Blindfold your subject and place one container in each hand. The weights should feel the same.
4. Take the beakers back. Add 20 ml of water to beaker A, and then ask if the weights feel the same or different. If the subject says "Different," ask which is heavier. If the subject is correct, remove the containers, place them back on the subject's hands, and ask again (to determine whether the subject's answer was simply a lucky guess).
5. If the subject cannot tell the difference between containers or his or her guess was wrong, add another 20 ml of water to beaker A. Continue to test the subject until he or she can detect a difference between container weights.
6. What is the "detection threshold" (the amount at which the subject can distinguish a difference in weight)? Does it differ from one person to the next? Hypothesize about why such differences exist. How could you test your hypothesis?

LAB EXERCISE 16.4

(20 minutes)

Investigating Sensory Integration

Information from both the general senses and the special senses is integrated by your brain to help you make sense of your surroundings. We are usually unaware of how multiple senses are employed in this integration. This simple demonstration will allow you to see how taste, smell, and vision are integrated when we determine flavor.

Materials:
- *Jellybeans, eight flavors, three of each per student pair (unique flavors are preferable: banana, coffee, licorice)*
- *Small envelopes, eight per student pair, labeled A, B, C, D, E, F, G, H*
- *Blindfolds*

Note: As with exercise 16.3, this demonstration could provide the setup for a simple student-designed experiment.

A. Work with a partner for this exercise. Obtain a set of envelopes labeled A through H from your lab instructor. Assign four of these envelopes to each lab partner.

B. Put on the blindfold. Plug your nose and have your lab partner feed you a jellybean from one of your packets. To the best of your ability, identify the flavor of the jellybean and have your partner write your response in Table 16.4. (Please speak softly so that other student pairs are not influenced by your answer.) Repeat this for the other three envelopes.

C. For the next round, remove the blindfold, but keep your nose plugged. What do you think the flavor of these candies is now? Write your response on the table.

TABLE 16.4 **Flavor Evaluation**

Envelope Letter	Taste Only	Taste and Sight	Taste, Sight, and Smell

D. Finally, eat the jellybeans without plugging your nose. Note the flavor on the chart.

E. Discuss the following questions:

1. Did the perceived flavor change over the course of the experiment? Why do you think?

2. Were some flavors easier to diagnose with fewer senses than others?

3. Compare your tables to those of other students in the class. Were some students better than others at discriminating taste with less information? Hypothesize about why there might be a difference. How might you test this hypothesis?

(20 minutes to 1 hour, depending on instructor's interests)

LAB EXERCISE 16.5

Memory and Learning

Materials:
- *Several lists of 20 words (see suggestions in Appendix B, page 246)*
- *Scrap paper for students for recording word lists, collecting data*
- *Radio/CD player, stop watch (optional, depends on student ideas)*

Instructors: The list can be any words you choose—all concrete, a mix of concrete and abstract words, or all abstract words. Of course, the more abstract and complex the list is, the fewer words your students will remember. You will need to have this initial list in tabular form to collect data from the students; an example is provided in Appendix B, p 246.

You should read the words in the order you have them in the table—students will see how the order of hearing influences which words are remembered. (Alternatively, if you mix them up, keep track of the order you read them in.)

How memory develops is still a mystery to neuroscientists. What is clear is that a memorable event or fact causes a change in brain biochemistry and that the areas of the brain that are involved in memory and learning can be activated by a variety of sensory triggers. Neuroscientists have also learned a number of different strategies for improving an individual's ability to recall information. You probably have ideas about how best to remember as well. In this exercise, you will design and perform an experiment as a class on the topic of memory and learning.

A. Your lab instructor will read you a list of 20 words. Do not write these down as they are being read! After the list is finished, you should silently write down as many words from this list as you remember, in any order. Do not share your list with your classmates.

B. Your lab instructor will now put the list on the board in the order in which it was read and collect information from you about which words you remembered.

C. Discuss the following questions:

1. Do you see a pattern in the results? Were some words remembered by more students than others? Why do you think there is a difference?
   Students might need some help here—are concrete words more likely to be remembered than abstract words? Ones heard first or last versus those in the middle? Similar words (for example, all fruits?) in an otherwise random-seeming list?

2. Choose one of the hypothesized explanations for why there is a difference in word recall, and design an experiment to test your hypothesis.
   Students may think of a variety of things—the recency/primary effect (we remember the beginning and end of a list more than the middle), the ability to chunk information (if your list contained say four fruits, four items of clothing, four male names, and so on), the importance of the involvement of other senses or noises, whether repeating the words makes a difference, reading versus hearing, and so on.

D. Perform the experiment you have designed. Do the results support or cause you to reject your hypothesis? Explain.

TOPIC 16

POST-LABORATORY QUIZ

THE HUMAN NERVOUS SYSTEM

1. Describe how a nerve impulse is transmitted along a neuron.

   A stimulus causes sodium channels on the neuron membrane to open, allowing positively charged sodium ions to enter the cell. As these ions migrate away from the channel, they trigger nearby sodium channels to open, allowing sodium in elsewhere in the cell body. This creates a domino effect known as an action potential, which self-propagates.

2. Describe how a nerve impulse is transferred from one neuron to another.

   When a nerve impulse reaches the end of a neuron, it triggers the release of a chemical called a neurotransmitter. These chemicals bind to receptors on adjacent neurons and start an action potential in these neurons.

3. What would happen to nerve transmission if a neurotransmitter remained in a synapse for longer than is typical?

   The duration of the nerve signal would be longer than is typical.

4. Novocaine, a drug used by dentists to "numb" the mouth before pain-causing work, blocks the opening of sodium channels on sensory neurons. How does this reduce pain?

   Neurons that sense pain will not be able to sustain an action potential, so pain signals are not received and processed by the brain, despite pain-causing activities occurring.

5. Dopamine is a neurotransmitter that stimulates neurons that trigger a sense of well-being and happiness. How would a drug that binds with dopamine receptors in the brain affect an individual in the short term?

   As a dopamine mimic, it should "turn on" the same neurons, leading to a sense of well-being and happiness—a "high."

6. How does repeated use of a dopamine mimic affect the neurons described previously?

   Individuals become less able to respond to normal dopamine levels—their response to pleasure is dulled and the only pleasure they feel is in response to higher and higher doses of the mimic.

7. List the three major brain regions and briefly describe their function.

- *Brain stem: heartbeat, breathing, swallowing, other automatic functions.*
- *Cerebellum: balance, muscle movement, coordination.*
- *Cerebrum: language, memory, sensations, decision making.*

8. How is a reflex different from a response that involves brain activity?

   A reflex essentially is a "short circuit" of the brain—there is no integration of information or decision making. The response is automatic and controlled by a single circuit of neurons, including a sensory neuron, an interneuron (typically), and a motor neuron, which causes an effect.

9. Describe how several senses interact to produce the sensation of "flavor."

   Sensory receptors for taste, smell, and sight all provide information to the brain to decode the complex experience of flavor. No one of these senses is sufficient to produce the full brain response.

10. Describe how you could test a hypothesis that consuming caffeine interferes with the development of memory.

    Look for controls (for example, use of caffeinated and uncaffeinated beverages, random assignment), a measure for determining differences in recall ability, and so on.

TOPIC 17

Plant Structure and Function

Learning Objectives

1. Appreciate the value of flowering plants to human and natural communities.
2. Examine flowering plant roots, stems, leaves, flowers, and fruits.
3. Learn about adaptations to plant organs.
4. Understand the requirements for maximum photosynthetic production in plants.
5. Investigate the role of water in plant structure and function.

A pre-laboratory quiz is available in Appendix A on page 229.

Pre-laboratory Reading

Flowering plants are among the most important organisms on Earth. They provide humans with nearly all of our agricultural products. They are a source of thousands of medicinal compounds. And, most importantly, they form the base of nearly all ecological communities on Earth's land surface. Alas, for many biology students, the study of the biology of plants seems dull—at best—and meaningless, at worst. Perhaps this is true because plants seem so inert; compared to animals they seem to be, well, "stick-in-the-muds." In this set of lab exercises, you will explore a small sampling of the structure and function of plants. We hope that by completing these exercises you will begin to see plants for the dynamic and fascinating organisms that they are.

Compared to animals, flowering plants have a very simple structure: only three non-reproductive organs—**roots, stems**, and **leaves**—made up of a few specialized tissues. The tissues include **vascular tissue**, made up of the water-carrying **xylem** and the nutrient-distributing **phloem**, and **epidermal tissue**, which has the competing functions of protecting the plant from harsh aspects of the environment while allowing the uptake of water, nutrients, and carbon dioxide. Natural selection on plants in different environments has shaped their organs and tissues into a dizzying array of shapes and functions.

Plants produce food via the process of **photosynthesis**, in which the energy from sunlight is captured in the chemical bonds of carbohydrates made from the raw materials of carbon dioxide and water. Creating conditions that maximize the total amount of photosynthesis our plants perform, and at appropriate times of the year, is the key purpose of agricultural practices. Of all agricultural practices, ensuring access to adequate water is primary. Plants require water not just as a raw material for photosynthesis, but also to give the plant shape. Adequate water inside plant cells helps provide support for soft tissues, such as leaves. Plants wilt when adequate water is not available, and a wilted plant has a much reduced rate of photosynthesis relative to a well-watered plant.

The mechanism for moving water from the soil to the shoots of a plant, called **transpiration**, relies on the pull exerted by evaporation—meaning that plants require many times more water than one would expect if water was necessary only for photosynthesis and to maintain the plant's shape. Plants do have some ability to control the rate at which water evaporates from the leaves. Pores on the leaves called **stomata** (singular: **stoma**) allow water to escape (and also allow carbon dioxide into the leaf for photosynthesis). The size of a stoma is controlled actively by **guard cells**, which surround and define the pore (Figure 17.1).

When water is abundant:

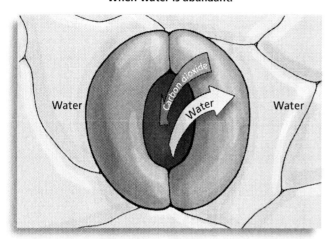

- Guard cells swell.
- Stoma (pore) is large.
- High carbon dioxide uptake
- High water loss

When water is scarce:

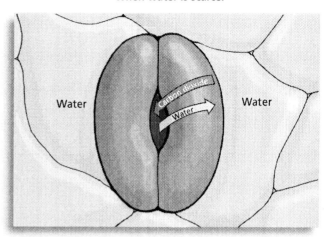

- Guard cells shrink.
- Stoma (pore) is small.
- Low carbon dioxide uptake
- Low water loss

FIGURE 17.1

(30 minutes to 2 hours, depending on number of specimens and portions of exercise completed)

Materials:

- *A variety of living flowering plants, illustrating basic stem anatomy (Coleus is a good choice, especially if Coleus slides are available), root structure (plant with tap root—could be Coleus) and one with fibrous roots (e.g. grass), and leaf structure (e.g. simple leaf, lobed leaves, pinnately and palmately compound leaves). These are primarily for demonstration, but you may be fortunate to have enough of one or a few types of plants to allow students to pull them out of the soil and dissect them. In periods of good weather, we have taken students into the campus natural area to poke and prod the local plants, and we found that students responded positively to this hands-on exploration.*
- *Microscope slides for demonstration or individual student examination: Coleus stem tip long section and stem cross section, dicot root tip long section and cross section, leaf cross section.*
- *A variety of vegetative organ adaptations: potatoes (underground storage stem), storage root (e.g. beet or carrot), onions (underground storage stem with leaves), cactus (illustrating spiny leaves and inflated, water-storing stem), poinsettia (leaves modified for insect attraction), pitcher plant (leaves modified as insect traps), etc.*
- *Flowers for dissection. We have had success growing abundant Fuschia flowers throughout the year. You also may be able to scavenge older flowers from florists or supermarkets.*
- *Fruit for dissection. Apples, oranges, cucumbers, cherry tomatoes, peanuts, sunflower seeds, etc.*

LAB EXERCISE 17.1

Explore Plant Structure

A. Examine basic root, stem, and leaf morphology and anatomy.

1. Root anatomy and morphology.

   a. Examine samples of tap roots and fibrous roots. Sketch the general appearance of these roots below.

   b. What advantages does a tap root have over a fibrous root system?
      Extends deeper into the soil, provides a solid base of support for the above-ground portion of the plant.

   c. What advantages does a fibrous root system have over a tap root?
      Can access greater quantities of water at the soil surface, potentially excluding competitors for light. Better able to recover from root damage.

   d. Examine a slide of the long section of a root tip. The loosely arranged cells at the very tip of the root are called the **root cap**. The cap is exterior to the actively dividing cells in the root's **apical meristem**. Cells produced by the apical meristem elongate, pushing the root tip through the soil. Above this zone of elongation, cells in the epidermis ("outer skin") of the root develop extensions called **root hairs**.

      Sketch the root tip below, identifying the root cap, apical meristem, zone of elongation, and root hairs.

e. What do you think the purpose of the root cap is?

Protection of the cells of the apical meristem as the root moves through the abrasive soil.

f. How might the extensions of the epidermis (root hairs) affect a root's ability to uptake water?

Increases the surface area of the root's "skin," providing more membrane across which water can cross.

g. Examine a slide of the cross section of a root. Here, the epidermis forms the outer layer surrounding a cortex, which in turn surrounds the vascular cylinder. The vascular cylinder contains xylem tubes arranged in a cross shape and phloem cells found in the axils of the cross.

   Sketch the cross section below, identifying the epidermis, cortex, vascular cylinder, xylem, and phloem.

2. Stem anatomy and morphology.
   a. Examine a "typical" stem. The organization of a stem is very regular, with **nodes** (where leaves and **axillary buds** are produced) alternating with **internodes**. The distance between internodes tends to decrease closer to the shoot tip. At the tip, a **terminal bud** contains the stem's apical meristem, which is producing cells in this alternating pattern.

      Sketch the stem below, identifying a node, leaf, axillary bud, internode, and terminal bud.

   b. Each axillary bud is a quiescent apical meristem, able to produce its own node/internode system. How might this arrangement be beneficial to a plant?

   Axillary buds can take over for damaged terminal buds. In addition, some axillary buds can be allowed to grow, permitting the plant to "grow into" the light resources that are available.

   c. Examine a microscope slide of stem tip long section. Note the domed apical meristem at the tip, the tiny leaves just below, and the axillary buds formed at the base of older leaves.

      Sketch the long section, labeling apical meristem, leaf, and axillary bud.

   d. The stem apical meristem does not produce a "stem cap" as the root apical meristem does. Why do you think this is the case?

   The stem apical meristem is not subject to the same abrasive forces as the root apical meristem. In addition, the tiny leaves produced by the stem meristem provide some protection of these cells from the harsher aspects of their environment.

   e. Examine a microscope slide of a stem cross section. Here, the vascular bundles are arranged just below the epidermal surface and the cortex takes up the center of the stem. In each vascular bundle, xylem cells are on the inner side and phloem is in the outside. The epidermis is coated with a thick layer of wax called the **cuticle**.

Sketch the cross section, labeling epidermis, cortex, and vascular bundles.

f. How is the epidermis of the stem different from the epidermis of the root?

No "hairs" but also modified with a cuticle (to restrict water loss).

3. Leaf anatomy and morphology.

a. Examine the leaves on the plants available. Note that not every single **blade** is an individual leaf—you can determine whether a leaf is made up of single or multiple blades by identifying where the main leaf stem, the **petiole**, attaches to the main stem of the plant. At this point, an axillary bud should be visible.

Sketch a variety of leaf shapes and blade arrangements that you see. On each, label the petiole.

b. Divided leaves allow a plant to produce a large leaf area for a relatively small amount of stem tissue. Why might a divided leaf be preferable to a single, very large blade?

A single blade is more likely to be damaged by strong winds or rain, while a multi-blade leaf is more flexible and lighter. In addition, multiple blades allow light to filter through a plant canopy, allowing more photosynthetic surface area to be functional.

c. Examine a microscope slide of a leaf cross section. The epidermis is pocked with stomata, visible as small gaps in the epidermal surface.

Sketch the leaf, identifying the epidermis and a stoma.

d. What is the advantage to the plant of having stomata primarily located on the undersurface of the leaf?

Stomata are shaded, reducing water evaporation. They also do not interfere with the photosynthetic cells that are receiving the maximum light on the upper surface of the leaf.

Instructors: This exercise is left open-ended for two reasons: (1) the materials may vary from class to class, and (2) students are encouraged to develop their own evolutionary hypotheses, rather than following the lead of the lab manual or instructor.

B. Learn about adaptations to roots, stems, and leaves.

Examine the variety of root, stem, and leaf adaptations made available in the lab. For each adaptation, list the organ it is modified from, the function of the adaptation, and the advantage you think it provides to the plant compared to other plants in the environment that lack the adaptation, in Table 17.1 below. Be prepared to discuss your hypotheses with your instructor and fellow students.

TABLE 17.1

Adaptation	Modified from what organ?	Function in the plant?	Advantage?

C. Dissect flowers and fruit.

1. The primary function of **flowers** is to facilitate pollination, the transfer of pollen from the male structures (**anthers**) to the female structure (**carpel**).

   a. Dissect a flower and identify the **sepals**, which are the lowermost "whorl" of parts and typically enclose the flower in a bud as it develops; the **petals**, typically modified to attract pollinators; anthers; and carpel.

   Sketch a cross section of the flower below, labeling sepals, petals, anthers, and carpel.

   b. Does it appear that this flower is adapted to attract insects, birds, or mammals? What evidence supports your answer?
   Depends on flower used. Typically bird flowers are bigger, redder, and more tubular than insect flowers. Mammal flowers often have a very strong, sweet smell to attract animals that rely heavily on scent.

c. Examine the carpel more closely by slicing it in cross section. Look for ovules, the structures that will form the seeds, inside.

2. **Fruits** develop from the flower's carpel (and sometimes associated structures) and are adapted to facilitate seed dispersal.

Examine (and dissect, if possible) the fruit available in lab. Find the seeds and any remaining flower parts. For each fruit examined, try to determine how it facilitates seed dispersal (i.e. does it attract an animal, float on water, ride on the wind, etc.?)

(30 Minutes)

LAB EXERCISE 17.2

Photosynthesis

Instructors: Topic 2, Cells and Energy, contains an additional exercise on photosynthesis.

Materials:

- *Variegated Coleus plants—enough for 1 leaf per student group*
- *Hot plates (4)*
- *Water baths (4—1 per hot plate)*
- *Methanol (Note: Methanol bath can become essentially "saturated" with chlorophyll. When this happens, chlorophyll will not diffuse from leaves. Refresh this solution frequently to avoid this difficulty.)*
- *500-mL beakers (4)*
- *Watch glasses (4—to cover beakers of hot methanol)*
- *Tongs (1 per student group)*
- *Petri dishes (1 per student group)*
- *Iodine (1 dropper bottle per student group)*

A. Obtain a leaf from a Variegated Coleus plant. The plant should have been under bright illumination for the past several hours. Draw the leaf here, indicating the pattern of pigmentation on the leaf.

B. Place the leaf in a hot water bath and allow the leaf to simmer for approximately one minute. If the leaf contains any purple pigment, keep the leaf in the water bath until all the pigment is gone from the leaf.

C. Using the tongs, transfer the leaf to a beaker containing methanol. Please be sure to replace the watch glass on top of the beaker to minimize evaporation of the methanol. Keep the leaf in the methanol until all of the chlorophyll (the green pigment) has diffused out of the leaf.

D. Using the tongs, transfer the leaf to a Petri dish. Note that after this processing, the leaf is flimsy. Carefully flatten the leaf, top side up, in the Petri dish.

E. Add several drops of iodine to the Petri dish, enough to cover the leaf completely with a thin layer of iodine.

F. You should observe a color change in the leaf. Draw the leaf here, indicating the pattern of pigmentation in the leaf.

G. Answer the following questions and be prepared to share your answers with your laboratory instructor and classmates:

1. Iodine combines with starch to produce a blue-black pigment. Given this information, describe where starch is found in the leaf. How does the pattern of starch production correlate to the original pigmentation of the leaf?

Starch is found in the areas of the leaf that contained green pigment, but not in areas where green pigment was absent.

2. Starch is the end product of photosynthesis. What do the pattern of starch accumulation and its correlation to leaf pigmentation tell you about the requirements for photosynthesis?

The green pigment, chlorophyll, is required for photosynthesis.

3. Magnesium is a chemical element required for the production of the green pigment, called chlorophyll, in plants. What do you expect would happen to a plant growing in soil that was lacking in magnesium?

It would produce little or no chlorophyll, and likely have limited growth.

LAB EXERCISE 17.3

Water and Plants

(90 Minutes)

A. Discover water transport in plants.

Your lab instructor has placed a plant in dyed water to help demonstrate the process of transpiration. Examine the plant and answer the following questions:

1. Where is the dye located in the plant?

Leaves of celery, petals of carnation

2. The location of the dye tells you something about where on the plant most of the "suction" occurs. Where is this?

Leaves or petals

3. What do you expect would happen to this plant if you removed it from the beaker of dye?

It would wilt.

(10 Minutes)

Materials:
- *500-mL beaker*
- *Food dye (red or blue)*
- *Celery with leaves OR white carnation*
- *Razor*

Instructors: Set up this demonstration at least three hours before the beginning of lab. Fill the beaker with water and add food dye until the solution is brightly pigmented. Place the celery or carnation in the beaker and, while the stem is submerged, use a razor to cut the bottom 2 cm off the stem. Keep the plant in a lighted environment.

B. The control of transpiration.

In this exercise, you will hypothesize about the number of stomata found on leaves of different types, and then examine these leaves for stomata.

1. Examine the leaves available for this investigation. Discuss with your lab partner how they might differ in the concentration of stomata on their surfaces—that is, the number of pores in a given area. Consider the factors that could influence the number of stomata, including potential for water loss and potential for photosynthesis.

2. Develop a hypothesis that you can test about how some or all of the leaves will differ in stomata concentration. Include in your hypothesis your reasoning for WHY you think they will differ in the manner you predict. Write your hypothesis here.

(40 Minutes)

Materials:
- *A variety of leaves of different types—for example, different sizes, from different habitats (desert versus rainforest), different pigmentations, and so on. You can provide these to the students or have them collect leaves from around campus.*
- *Clear nail polish (1 bottle per student group)*
- *Microscope slides and cover slips (2 or 3 per student group)*
- *Dropper bottle of water (1 per student group)*
- *Compound microscope (1 per student group)*
- *Graph paper or computer with spread sheet program (optional—1 per group)*

3. To calculate the concentration of stomata on the leaves, follow this protocol:

a. Paint a 1 cm square of the undersurface of the leaf with clear nail polish.

b. Allow the nail polish to dry and then peel it off to produce a "cast" of the leaf. Do not worry if the cast tears; you only need a small amount to make the estimate.

c. Place the cast on a microscope slide, add a drop of water, and cover with a cover slip.

d. Place the slide on the microscope stage and find the cast under lowest power. Center the cast in the field of view and change the magnification on the scope to the highest power (*not* the oil immersion lens, if you have one).

e. Count all of the stomata in the field of view, and then move the slide on the stage slightly so that you are observing a different region of the cast. Count all of the stomata in this field. Continue counting stomata in two more fields of view. Put your data in Table 17.2.

TABLE 17.2

Leaf Type:	Leaf Type:	Leaf Type:
Average number of stomata/field of view:	Average number of stomata/field of view:	Average number of stomata/field of view:

Instructors: This activity provides an opportunity to work with students to find the best way to graphically represent data.

f. Calculate the average number of stomata per field of view.

4. Your lab instructor might ask you to present this data in a graphical format.

5. Did the results of your hypothesis test match your predictions? If not, speculate as to why your hypothesis was incorrect. Be prepared to present your hypothesis test to the class.

C. Determine the factors that influence the rate of transpiration.

The rate of transpiration from plants in a natural environment is influenced by a number of factors. In this exercise, you will make and test a hypothesis about which factors increase the rate of transpiration and which decrease the rate of transpiration.

1. Discuss the weather conditions that you think would increase or decrease the rate of transpiration from a plant. Come up with a testable hypothesis that describes a condition that you believe will increase transpiration and one that you believe will decrease transpiration. Write your hypotheses here.

(40 Minutes)

Materials:
- *Water baths, large enough to submerge an entire 1-mL glass pipette in—4 per lab*
- *Pipettor bulbs—4 or 5*
- *Vaseline*
- *Fan*
- *Bright light*
- *Cardboard boxes (large enough to enclose ring stand and plant)*
- *Plant mister*
- *Hair dryer*

These materials are required by each student group:
- *Sunflower seedling, 3 weeks old*
- *1-mL glass pipette, graduated in 0.01-mL increments*
- *Ring stand with small ring*
- *Rubber tubing, 5-cm section, diameter approximately equal to pipette and seedling*
- *Razor*
- *Kimwipes*

Instructors: If students need some help with step 1, you can encourage their creativity by letting them know what materials you have for simulating various weather conditions.

2. Obtain a sunflower seedling, a 1-mL glass pipette, a ring stand with ring, and a small section of rubber tubing. You will use these materials to make a "transpiration meter."

3. Submerge the pipette in the water bath and use a pipettor bulb to draw a continuous column of water into the pipette. Do not draw water past

the last graduation mark on the pipette. Keep the pipette underwater as you complete the rest of the setup.

4. Submerge the cut end of the sunflower seedling into the water bath and use the razor to cut the lower 2 cm of the seedling. Use the rubber tubing as a connector between the narrow end of the pipette and the cut end of the seedling.

5. Remove the entire apparatus from the water bath. Wipe water from the outside of the pipette. If water is dripping from the end of the pipette, the column of water is not continuous—you will need to start over.

6. Wait five minutes to allow the seedling to acclimate to the change. You will now measure the amount of water (in mL) lost from the column in the environmental conditions you specified in your hypothesis.

7. Place your plant in one of the environmental conditions you specified. Record the amount of water lost from the pipette every three minutes for nine minutes total. Calculate the average amount of water lost for a three-minute period and record in Table 17.3.

Instructors: If students in the lab section are all testing the same hypothesis, place half of the seedlings in one condition and half in the other.

TABLE 17.3

End of Time Period	mL of Water Lost
3 minutes	
6 minutes	
9 minutes	
Average for 3-minute period	

8. Place your plant in the second of the environmental conditions you specified. After a five-minute acclimation period, begin another nine-minute recording period (use Table 17.4).

TABLE 17.4

End of Time Period	mL of Water Lost
3 minutes	
6 minutes	
9 minutes	
Average for 3-minute period	

9. Answer the following questions and be prepared to share your answers with your lab instructor and fellow classmates:

a. Which condition had the greatest effect on transpiration rate?

b. Does this result support your hypothesis? If not, explain why you think the results were different from what you expected.

TOPIC 17

_____

POST-LABORATORY QUIZ

PLANT STRUCTURE AND FUNCTION

1. Sketch the aboveground portions of a stem, labeling: node, internode, axillary bud, terminal bud, petiole, and blade.

2. What is the function of the root cap on the tip of a growing root?
   Protects the apical meristem from abrasion by the soil.

3. Potatoes are underground structures adapted to store starch. What features of a potato should identify it as a stem rather than a root?
   Presence of axillary buds, node/internode arrangement, more than one vascular bundle.

4. Sketch a flower, labeling: sepals, petals, anthers, carpel, and ovule.

5. Starch is only produced in parts of a plant that contain chlorophyll. What does this information tell you about the role of chlorophyll in a plant?
   Starch is the end product of photosynthesis; therefore, chlorophyll is required for photosynthesis to occur.

6. In the photosynthesis activity, what would have happened if we had covered some of the leaves with aluminum foil a few days before lab?
   Photosynthesis would not have occurred in these leaves. Upon treatment, the leaves would not have reacted with the iodine to indicate the presence of starch.

7. Describe how water moves up the stem of a plant from the roots to the leaves.

   Evaporation of water through pores in the leaf (that is, stomata) creates a pulling action that draws water up the stem from the roots. This process is called transpiration.

8. On St. Patrick's Day in many places, florists offer carnations that have green speckled petals. These carnations are naturally white, but their petals have not been "dipped" into a green dye or paint. Use your understanding of water movement in plants to describe how florists produce these carnations.

   The carnations are placed in a solution of green dye and allowed to transpire. As water evaporates from the petals, the green dye is pulled up the xylem and into the petals, where it becomes visible in the veins and on the tips of the petals.

9. Name at least two environmental factors that are likely to cause a high rate of transpiration in plants and explain why they do.
   - *High temperature increases rate of evaporation from leaves.*
   - *Low humidity increases rate of evaporation from leaves.*
   - *Bright sunlight increases photosynthesis, requiring high levels of carbon dioxide. To get greater amounts of carbon dioxide, plants will open stomata, increasing rate of water loss.*

10. Imagine two plants in approximately the same climate conditions. One grows in open meadows and is exposed to full sunlight and brisk winds, while the other grows on the forest floor, beneath the shade of large trees and sheltered from the wind. Which would likely have a greater density of stomata and why?

    The plant growing on the forest floor would be expected to have more densely packed stomata, since the environmental factors that promote water loss should be lower in that environment and greater in the field environment.

APPENDIX A

Name:_____

Section: _____

TOPIC 1

PRE-LABORATORY QUIZ

THE SCIENTIFIC METHOD

1. Which of the following are characteristics of a scientific hypothesis?
   a. It must be true.
   b. It must be testable through objective observations about the world.
   c. It cannot invoke a supernatural cause or effect.
   d. It is a tentative explanation about how something works or why a particular event occurred.
   e. More than one of the above is correct.

2. The statement "Biology lab is more fun than a barrel of monkeys" is not a scientific hypothesis. Why not?
   a. It was not proposed by a scientist.
   b. It cannot be tested objectively as stated.
   c. It is not true.
   d. Statements that cannot be tested with experiments are not scientific.
   e. There are no data to support the hypothesis.

3. Experimental controls _____:
   a. ensure that the data collected are statistically significant
   b. ensure that the data are collected objectively
   c. help minimize the chance that another factor could explain a difference between treated and untreated individuals
   d. are used to make predictions about the outcome of an experiment
   e. prevent scientists from falsifying their results

4. Measurements collected for tests of hypotheses are called _____:
   a. data
   b. statistics
   c. controls
   d. predictions
   e. samples

5. Statistical tests test for _____:
   a. whether the hypothesis is true
   b. whether the data were collected objectively
   c. whether the hypothesis is scientific
   d. whether the experiment was well controlled
   e. whether the difference between the experimental and control group is larger than expected by chance

TOPIC 2

PRE-LABORATORY QUIZ

CELLS AND ENERGY

1. "Biology" is defined as the study of:
   a. cells
   b. life
   c. heredity
   d. evolution
   e. animals and plants

2. The structure inside of cells that contains the DNA is called:
   a. the karyote
   b. the kernel
   c. the nucleus
   d. the membrane
   e. the cell sac

3. Cells that contain a nucleus are called:
   a. eukaryotes
   b. prokaryotes
   c. superkaryotes
   d. viruses
   e. more than one of the above is correct

4. Homeostasis is:
   a. the ability to move
   b. reproduction
   c. a category of living organisms
   d. the maintenance of internal conditions
   e. the ability to convert solar energy to chemical energy

5. Homeostasis requires:
   a. sunlight
   b. a constant energy input
   c. the consumption of other organisms
   d. cells with nuclei
   e. an unchanging external environment

TOPIC 3

PRE-LABORATORY QUIZ

NUTRITION AND METABOLISM

1. Enzymes:
    a. Are able to catalyze reactions involving many different substrates in the same active site
    b. Are composed of differently ordered carbohydrates
    c. Have active sites that are specific to one substrate
    d. Of different individuals catalyze reactions at the same rate
    e. Are composed of different numbers of one individual amino acid

2. The cellular organelle that converts the products of digestion into ATP is:
    a. Found only in plants
    b. Found in plants and animals
    c. The endoplasmic reticulum
    d. The nucleus
    e. The amino acid

3. Cellular respiration:
    a. Uses oxygen to produce ATP and releases carbon dioxide
    b. Occurs in mitochondria found in the nucleus
    c. Releases the oxygen we breathe as a by-product
    d. Results in the production of sugars from carbon dioxide and water
    e. Both b and c are correct

4. Denaturation of an enzyme:
    a. Changes the order of amino acids in the enzyme
    b. Changes the order of nucleotides in the enzyme
    c. Might alter the shape of the active site
    d. Allows the enzyme to catalyze the same reaction many times
    e. Usually speeds up the rate at which the enzyme catalyzes the reaction

5. A person's weight might be affected by:
    a. The rate at which their enzymes catalyze metabolic reactions
    b. Heart rate and exercise level
    c. The number of metabolic enzymes active in their cells
    d. The number of calories consumed
    e. All of the above are true

TOPIC 4

PRE-LABORATORY QUIZ

MITOSIS

1. The process of cell division in eukaryotes is known as:
   a. Interphase
   b. Mitosis
   c. Prophase
   d. Epidemiology
   e. Tumor suppression

2. During interphase of the cell cycle:
   a. DNA is replicated
   b. Chromosomes condense
   c. Sister chromatids are separated
   d. The cell physically divides into two daughter cells
   e. Proto-oncogenes mutate

3. Metaphase and anaphase result in the separation of:
   a. Microtubules
   b. Cytokinesis
   c. Sister chromatids
   d. Nuclear membranes
   e. Daughter cells

4. A proto-oncogene:
   a. Causes cancer
   b. Is a known risk factor
   c. Is not found in normal cells
   d. Helps to control cell division in normal cells
   e. Is not replicated during interphase of the cell cycle

5. Cancer:
   a. Results from mutations in genes that control the cell cycle
   b. Results from mutations in genes that stop cells with damaged DNA from dividing
   c. Can result from exposure to environmental factors that cause DNA damage
   d. a and b are correct
   e. a, b, and c are correct

TOPIC 5

PRE-LABORATORY QUIZ

MEIOSIS AND GENETICS

1. DNA:
    a. Is passed from an adult to his or her siblings
    b. Stands for deoxygenated nuclear assortment
    c. Is what genes are made of
    d. Is dominant when wrapped around proteins
    e. All of the above are true

2. Chromosomes:
    a. Carry hundreds of genes along their length
    b. Can be arranged in pairs carrying the same genes, called homologous pairs
    c. Are composed of DNA and protein
    d. Of a homologous pair are separated from each other during meiosis
    e. All of the above are true

3. Meiosis:
    a. Occurs in body cells
    b. Always separates dominant from recessive alleles
    c. Occurs in the ovaries and testes and produces cells with homologous pairs of chromosomes
    d. Only occurs in yeast
    e. Is a type of cell division that produces gametes

4. The genotype:
    a. Is the assortment of alleles present in a given individual
    b. Is produced by the phenotype
    c. Is the appearance of the individual
    d. Is visible in the karyotype
    e. All of the above are true

5. Fertilization:
    a. Occurs inside the testes and ovaries
    b. Is followed by meiosis, which decreases the chromosome number
    c. Allows sperm and egg cells to combine their genetic information
    d. Occurs during meiosis
    e. Allows alleles of a gene to separate from each other

TOPIC 6

PRE-LABORATORY QUIZ

DNA STRUCTURE, SYNTHESIS, AND FINGERPRINTING

1. Which of the following is a false statement about DNA structure?
   a. DNA is composed of two anti-parallel strands.
   b. The sugars that comprise part of the backbone differ from one nucleotide to the next.
   c. Nitrogenous bases can have four different structures (A, G, C, and T).
   d. Nitrogenous bases are connected to each other by hydrogen bonds.
   e. Nucleotides are composed of a sugar, a phosphate, and a nitrogenous base.

2. DNA:
   a. Sequences for different genes can be the same
   b. Is single stranded
   c. Is found in the ribosomes of most cells
   d. Is composed of three parallel strands of nucleotides
   e. Codes for the production of proteins

3. If a parental DNA strand has the sequence CGT, the daughter strand will have the sequence:
   a. CGT
   b. TCA
   c. TGC
   d. GCA
   e. TGC

4. Deoxyribose:
   a. Is the sugar found in DNA
   b. Is a nucleotide
   c. Is part of a nitrogenous base
   d. Is found only in A, C, and T
   e. All of the above are true

5. DNA fingerprinting is based on the fact that no two (nonidentical twin) individuals:
   a. Have all the same DNA sequences
   b. Have some identical DNA sequences
   c. Can produce any of the same proteins
   d. Can produce any of the same mRNA molecules
   e. All of the above are true

TOPIC 7

PRE-LABORATORY QUIZ

TRANSCRIPTION, TRANSLATION, AND GENETICALLY MODIFIED ORGANISMS

1. DNA sequences that code for the production of proteins are called:
   a. RNAs
   b. Ribosomes
   c. Codons
   d. Proteinaceous materials
   e. Genes

2. Transcription:
   a. Converts mRNA into protein
   b. Occurs on structures called cytochromes
   c. Is the synthesis of an RNA molecule that is complementary to the DNA
   d. Is the synthesis of DNA from RNA
   e. Uses uracil in place of cytosine

3. Translation:
   a. Uses DNA to synthesize RNA
   b. Uses RNA to synthesize DNA
   c. Is the synthesis of protein using information coded for in RNA
   d. Is the synthesis of amino acids from ribosomes
   e. Incorporates uracils in place of thymines

4. The universality of the genetic code refers to the fact that:
   a. All organisms make the same proteins.
   b. All proteins are composed of the same order of amino acids.
   c. Different organisms incorporate the same amino acid in response to the same codon.
   d. The mRNA produced by transcription of bacterial proteins is always the same.
   e. Ribosomes of all living organisms are identical.

5. Genetically modified organisms:
   a. Are produced by high-tech breeding procedures
   b. Are organisms that have had their DNA manipulated
   c. Are produced by transcription
   d. Are produced by translation
   e. Are produced by changing which codons code for a given amino acid

TOPIC 8

PRE-LABORATORY QUIZ

THE THEORY OF EVOLUTION

1. The theory of common descent states that:
   a. Humans evolved from chimpanzees.
   b. All organisms are essentially the same.
   c. All modern organisms are related to each other.
   d. All modern organisms arose from common nonliving materials.
   e. Each species originated separately and has changed over descent.

2. The branch of science that concerns itself with attempting to understand the hypothetical evolutionary history of life is known as:
   a. Systematics
   b. Phylogeny
   c. Darwinism
   d. Hypothesis testing
   e. Common ancestry

3. A homology:
   a. Is a similarity in appearance due to shared environmental conditions
   b. Is a similarity that occurs as a result of shared common ancestry
   c. Provides evidence of evolutionary relationship among organisms
   d. b and c are correct
   e. a, b, and c are correct

4. On a phylogenetic tree, a branch point that unites two groups of organisms and that appears near the base of the tree indicates:
   a. A lack of evidence for a common ancestor
   b. Abundant evidence of a common ancestor
   c. A relatively recent common ancestor
   d. A relatively ancient common ancestor
   e. The universal common ancestor

5. Which of the following similarities between the organism pairs is most likely analogy rather than homology?
   a. Both bees and wasps have membranous wings.
   b. Both bats and whales use sonar to locate food.
   c. Both crocodiles and snakes are covered with scales.
   d. Both birds and fish have hearts.
   e. Both dandelions and daisies produce flowers for reproduction.

TOPIC 9

PRE-LABORATORY QUIZ

NATURAL SELECTION

1. The process of natural selection causes:
    a. Mutation
    b. Environmental change
    c. Higher fitness
    d. Competition
    e. Evolution

2. An adaptation is:
    a. The result of a mutation
    b. A trait that increases survival and/or reproduction
    c. Likely to become common in the population it appears in
    d. b and c are correct
    e. a, b, and c are correct

3. "Evolutionary fitness" is best defined as:
    a. Chance of survival and reproduction compared to other individuals in the same population
    b. Only the strongest survive
    c. The ability to escape predation
    d. Adaptation to the environment over time
    e. A change in allele frequency over the course of generations

4. An adaptation spreads throughout a population over time because:
    a. Other organisms see that it is successful and copy it
    b. Predators avoid killing individuals with particular adaptations
    c. It can be passed to the next generation in genes
    d. It allows individuals who possess it to live longer
    e. The population is human

5. The modern definition of the theory of evolution connects traits to genes and can be restated as:
    a. Some mutations can be harmful and some beneficial
    b. All traits result from genes
    c. Natural selection causes the appearance of new genes
    d. Evolution is the change in the frequency of particular alleles in a population
    e. Each species of organisms has a completely unique set of genes

TOPIC 10

PRE-LABORATORY QUIZ

SPECIES AND RACES

1. Biological species are defined by:
    a. Reproductive isolation from other species
    b. Physical separation from other species
    c. Differences in appearance from other species
    d. A lack of natural selection within the species
    e. Convergence with other, related species

2. After two or more populations of a species become physically isolated from each other:
    a. Their gene pools become separate
    b. They may evolve independently of one another
    c. They will inevitably become reproductively incompatible
    d. a and b are correct
    e. a, b, and c are correct

3. A biological race:
    a. Is equivalent to a species
    b. Is reproductively isolated from other biological races
    c. Can be easily distinguished by differences in coloration
    d. Is a population that has diverged from other populations of the same species
    e. Forms when males exhibit clear preferences for certain female characteristics

4. Which of the following is an example of convergent evolution?
    a. Two species of rose both have thorns.
    b. Penguins use their wings to swim, while their close relatives use their wings to fly.
    c. The parasitic plant Indian Pipe does not produce chlorophyll for photosynthesis.
    d. Ferruginous Hawks and Monarch Butterflies both migrate to Mexico during the northern winter.
    e. Blue Jays and blueberries are both blue.

5. Sexual selection acts on characteristics that influence:
    a. Mating success
    b. The likelihood a male will be selected as a mate by a female
    c. The likelihood a female will be selected as a mate by a male
    d. a and b are correct
    e. a, b, and c are correct

TOPIC 11

PRE-LABORATORY QUIZ

BIODIVERSITY

1. Among the characteristics that place individual species in different domains is (are):
   a. The presence or absence of a nucleus
   b. The ability to make their own food from sunlight
   c. Characteristics of the cell wall, if present
   d. a and c are correct
   e. a, b, and c are correct

2. "Biodiversity" refers to:
   a. The ability of humans to classify the living world
   b. The theorized evolutionary relationships among living organisms
   c. The variety of living organisms
   d. The racial diversity of biologists
   e. The survival of the fittest

3. Which of the following classification categories is most inclusive (that is, contains the broadest grouping of species)?
   a. Phylum
   b. Class
   c. Order
   d. Family
   e. Species

4. All of the following are kingdoms in the Domain Eukarya EXCEPT:
   a. Archaea
   b. Fungi
   c. Plantae
   d. Animalia
   e. Protista

5. The theory of evolution refers to:
   a. The hypothesis that humans evolved from chimpanzees
   b. The idea that all organisms were separately created
   c. The ability to classify organisms according to similarities
   d. The hypothesis that all organisms derive from a single common ancestral species
   e. The principle that only the strongest species survive

TOPIC 12

PRE-LABORATORY QUIZ

POPULATION AND ECOSYSTEM ECOLOGY

1. Human populations in the past two centuries have increased as a result of _____.
   a. an increase in birth rate
   b. a decrease in birth rate
   c. an increase in death rate
   d. a decrease in death rate
   e. more than one of the above is correct

2. The maximum population size an environment can support indefinitely is known as the _____ of that environment.
   a. exponent
   b. carrying capacity
   c. growth rate
   d. population max
   e. population overshoot

3. Growth rates of a population approaching an environmental limit decline as a result of _____
   a. a change in carrying capacity
   b. increasing death rates
   c. decreasing birth rates
   d. both b and c could be correct
   e. a, b, and c could be correct

4. All of the interacting living and non-living factors in a given environment are referred to as the:
   a. biological community
   b. food chain
   c. biomagnifier
   d. ecosystem
   e. carried capacity

5. Biomagnification:
   a. occurs as a result of how energy flows within ecosystems
   b. is the tendency for environmentalists to overstate environmental damage
   c. is only possible under controlled laboratory settings
   d. occurs as a result of disrupted nutrient cycles and results in the death of waterways
   e. is more of a problem for plants than for top predators

TOPIC 13

PRE-LABORATORY QUIZ

COMMUNITY ECOLOGY AND CONSERVATION BIOLOGY

1. An ecosystem is:
   a. a group of individuals of the same species
   b. all of the organisms and physical features in a given environment
   c. created by humans for the conservation of endangered species
   d. unable to survive when humans intervene
   e. a concept that has little biological meaning

2. Ecologists seek to explain the factors that influence:
   a. the distribution of particular species
   b. the abundance of particular species
   c. why species are found in particular regions of Earth
   d. a and c are correct
   e. a, b, and c are correct

3. Which of the following interactions between organisms is an example of competition?
   a. a bee gathering honey from, and spreading the pollen of, a flowering plant
   b. a cleaner fish picking small bits of food and parasites from the jaws of a reef shark
   c. chickadees and nuthatches taking seeds from a bird feeder
   d. wolves stalking and killing an elderly moose
   e. eagles and hawks migrating south for the winter

4. The loss of genetic diversity that occurs as a result of random changes is known as:
   a. genetic drift
   b. species endangerment
   c. loss of ecosystem services
   d. homozygosity
   e. allele infrequency

5. An increased rate of inbreeding:
   a. occurs when the population is so small that there is a high likelihood of close relatives mating
   b. can result in high levels of homozygosity
   c. can lead to inbreeding depression
   d. can result in poorly surviving offspring
   e. all of the above

TOPIC 14

PRE-LABORATORY QUIZ

GENDER DIFFERENCES AND ATHLETICISM

1. Which endocrine organ becomes active at puberty?
   a. the ovary
   b. the penis
   c. the oviduct
   d. the cervix
   e. the vagina

2. Which of the following is a false statement about female skeletal structure?
   a. A female's bones are composed of different minerals than a male's bones.
   b. A female's bones tend to be shorter than a male's bones.
   c. Females have a lower center of gravity than males.
   d. Females have a larger Q angle than males.
   e. A female's bones tend to have less muscle mass attached than a male's bones.

3. The female pelvis:
   a. has a less angled tilt than the male pelvis
   b. has a more oval opening than the male pelvis
   c. has fewer bones than the male pelvis
   d. is broader and flatter than the male pelvis
   e. has a different point of attachment to the tail bone than the male pelvis

4. Because puberty tends to start later in boys:
   a. boys make fewer gametes than girls
   b. boys have longer legs and arms than girls
   c. boys are less likely to play sports
   d. boys have a smaller Q angle than girls
   e. boys are less likely to use birth control than girls

5. True or False? The proteins found in female muscles are different in amino acid composition than those found in males.

TOPIC 15

PRE-LABORATORY QUIZ

FERTILIZATION, BIRTH CONTROL, AND SEXUALLY TRANSMITTED DISEASES

1. Pelvic Inflammatory Disease is caused by:
   a. infection with certain protozoans
   b. viral infection
   c. infection with either of two different bacteria
   d. simultaneous infection by bacteria and viruses
   e. infection with certain insects

2. Assume that a certain type of bacterium divides once every minute. If you start with one bacterial cell in culture, after six minutes there should be _____ bacterial cells.
   a. 6
   b. 12
   c. 32
   d. 64
   e. several million

3. Pubic lice:
   a. is also called the clap
   b. is caused by a protozoan
   c. transmission can be prevented with the use of condoms
   d. can affect both males and females
   e. all of the above are true

4. An epidemiologist tries to determine:
   a. the source of an infection
   b. who is at risk for infectious diseases
   c. when the disease might strike a population
   d. the cause of infectious (not genetic) diseases
   e. all of the above

5. Birth control methods can:
   a. block sperm and egg contact
   b. change the environment of the female reproductive tract, making it less hospitable to sperm
   c. prevent ovulation
   d. block gamete-carrying ducts
   e. all of the above

TOPIC 16

PRE-LABORATORY QUIZ

THE HUMAN NERVOUS SYSTEM

1. The cells of the nervous system are called:
    a. nerves
    b. neurons
    c. reflexes
    d. synapses
    e. neurotransmitters

2. A nerve impulse is transmitted along a neuron by:
    a. the release of neurotransmitters
    b. the reuptake of neurotransmitters
    c. the increased activity of synapses
    d. a change in electrical charge that is self-propagating
    e. the actions of the brain and spinal cord

3. Which organ integrates and processes sensory information?
    a. Brain
    b. Spinal cord
    c. Nerves
    d. Neurons
    e. Synapses

4. Drugs that affect the brain often are mimics of, or affect the longevity of:
    a. neurotransmitters
    b. special senses
    c. synapses
    d. neurons
    e. nerve impulses

5. Which of the following is a special sense, rather than a general sense?
    a. Temperature
    b. Pain
    c. Touch
    d. Taste
    e. Pressure

TOPIC 17

PRE-LABORATORY QUIZ

PLANT STRUCTURE AND FUNCTION

1. All of the following are plant organs or tissues EXCEPT:
   a. roots
   b. stems
   c. carbon dioxide
   d. phloem
   e. xylem

2. Water is essential to plants because:
   a. it is required to convert carbon dioxide to sugar in photosynthesis
   b. it provides support to the tissues of plants, giving the plant its shape
   c. the evaporation of large amounts of water provides the pulling force bringing water from the roots to the leaves
   d. a and b are correct
   e. a, b, and c are correct

3. The ultimate source of energy for life on Earth is:
   a. The sun
   b. Water
   c. Carbon dioxide
   d. Inorganic fertilizer
   e. Domestic animals

4. The process that moves water from the roots to the leaves of a plant is called:
   a. respiration
   b. photosynthesis
   c. transpiration
   d. evaporation
   e. circulation

5. Stomata on the surface of a plant:
   a. open and close to regulate carbon dioxide entry and water evaporation
   b. help absorb water from the soil
   c. protect the plant from damage by animals and fungi
   d. are eliminated by the immune system's guard cells
   e. are part of a plant-to-plant communication system

PRE-LABORATORY QUIZ ANSWERS

Topic 1: The Scientific Method
    1.e 2.b 3.c 4.a 5.e

Topic 2: Cells and Energy
    1.b 2.c 3.a 4.d 5.b

Topic 3: Nutrition and Metabolism
    1.c 2.b 3.a 4.c 5.e

Topic 4: Mitosis
    1.b 2.a 3.c 4.d 5.e

Topic 5: Meiosis and Genetics
    1.c 2.e 3.e 4.a 5.c

Topic 6: DNA Structure, Synthesis, and Fingerprinting
    1.b 2.e 3.d 4.a 5.a

Topic 7: Transcription, Translation, and Genetically Modified Organisms
    1.e 2.c 3.c 4.c 5.b

Topic 8: The Theory of Evolution
    1.c 2.a 3.d 4.d 5.b

Topic 9: Natural Selection
    1.e 2.e 3.a 4.c 5.d

Topic 10: Species and Races
    1.a 2.d 3.d 4.d 5.e

Topic 11: Biodiversity
    1.d 2.c 3.a 4.a 5.d

Topic 12: Population And Ecosystem Ecology
    1.d 2.b 3.d 4.d 5.a

Topic 13: Community Ecology and Conservation Biology
    1.b 2.e 3.c 4.a 5.e

Topic 14: Gender Differences and Athleticism
    1.a 2.a 3.d 4.b 5.False

Topic 15: Fertilization, Birth Control, and Sexually Transmitted Diseases
    1.c 2.d 3.d 4.e 5.e

Topic 16: The Human Nervous System
    1.b 2.d 3.a 4.a 5.d

Topic 17: Plant Structure and Function
    1.c 2.e 3.a 4.c 5.a

APPENDIX B

Constructing a 3-D Model of DNA

Sequence ID # M1:
T A T A A A A T G T T T G A G G C A A T G C T A C G T A A T C C G G T T T A T C C A T G A

Sequence ID # C1:
T A T A A A A T G T T T G A G G C A A T A C T A C G T A A T C C G G T T T A T C C C T G A

Sequence ID # W1:
T A T A A A A T G T T T G A G G C A A T G C T A C G T A A T C C G G T T T A T C C C T G A

Sequence ID # X1:
T A T A A A A T G T T T G A G G C A A T A C T A C G T A A T C C G G T T T A A C C C T G A

Sequence ID # Y1:
T A T A A A A T G T T T G A G G C A A T A C T A C G T A A A C C A G T T T A T C C C T G A

Sequence ID # Z1:
T A T A A A A T G T T T G A G G C A A T A C T A C G T A A A C C A G T T T A T C C C T G A

Sequence ID # M2:
T A T A A A A T G A C C C A A G T T G A T A G G C C C T G T T T C C C C T A A C G G T A G

Sequence ID # C2:
T A T A A A A T G A C C C A A G T T G A A A A G C C C T G T T T C C C C T A C C G G T A G

Sequence ID # W2:
T A T A A A A T G A C C C A A G T T G A T A A G C C C T G T T T C C C C T A C C G G T A G

Sequence ID # X2:
T A T A A A A T G A C C C A A G T T G A T A G G C C C T G T T T C C C C T A T C G G T A G

Sequence ID # Y2:
T A T A A A A T G A C C C A A G T T G A A A G G C C C T G T T T C C C C T A C C G G T A G

Sequence ID # Z2:
T A T A A A A T G G C C C A A G T T G A T A G G C C C T G T T T C C C C T A T C G G T A G

Sequence ID # M3:
T A T A A A A T G T C C T T A A G T T C T G G C C A T G G A T C C G T G G G G C A A T A A

Sequence ID # C3:
T A T A A A A T G T C C T T A A G T C C T G G C C A T G G A T C C G T G G G G C A A T A A

Sequence ID # W3:
T A T A A A A T G T C C T T A A G T T C T G G C C A C G G A T C C G T G G G G C A C T A A

Sequence ID # X3:
T A T A A A A T G G C C T T A A G T T C T G G C C A T G G A T C C G T G G G G C A C T A A

Sequence ID # Y3:
T A T A A A A T G T C C T T A A G T T C T G G C C A C G G A T C C G T G G G G C A C T A A

Sequence ID # Z3:
T A T A A A A T G T C C T T A A G T T C T G G C C A C G G A T C C G T G G G G C A C T A A

Sequence ID # M4:
T A T A A A A T G C C A G A C C A A A A A T A T A G A T C A C C G G G G A C A C T T T A G

Sequence ID # C4:
T A T A A A A T G C C A G A C C A G A A A T A T A G A T C A C C G G G G A C A C T T T A G

Sequence ID # W4:
T A T A A A A T G C C A G A C C A A A A A T A T A G A T G A C A G G G G A C A C T A T A G

Sequence ID # X4:
T A T A A A A T G C C A G A C C A A A A A T A A A G A T C A C A G G G G A C A C T A T A G

Sequence ID # Y4:
T A T A A A A T G C C A G A C C A A A A A T A A A G A T G A C C G G G G A C A C T T T A G

Sequence ID # Z4:
T A T A A A A T G C C A G G C C A G A A A T A T A G A T C A T C G G G G A C A C T T T A G

Test a Hypothesis of Evolutionary Relationship by Examining the Classification of the Species in Your Analysis

Classification Information

- Cat: Superorder Clade IV, Order Carnivora, Superfamily Felioidea, Family Felidae, Subfamily Filinae, Genus Felis, Species *Felis sylvestris*
- Dog: Superorder Clade IV, Order Carnivora, Superfamily Canoidea, Family Canidae, Genus Canis, Species *Canis lupus*
- Mink: Superorder Clade IV, Order Carnivora, Superfamily Canoidea, Family Mustelidae, Subfamily Mustelinae, Genus Mustela, Species *Mustela vison*
- Muskrat: Superorder Clade III, Order Rodentia, Suborder Sciurognathi, Family Muridae, Subfamily Arvicolinae, Genus Ondatra, Species *Ondatra zibethicus*
- Sheep: Superorder Clade IV, Order Artiodactyla, Family Bovidae, Subfamily Caprinae, Genus Ovis, Species *Ovis aries*
- Pig: Superorder Clade IV, Order Artiodactyla, Family Suidae, Subfamily Suinae, Genus Sus, Species *Sus scrofa*

The superorder "names" are from a paper on recent DNA sequence comparisons (Murphy, W.J. et al., *Nature* 409: 614-618) that identified broad relationships among the placental mammals.

Test Your Hypothesis of Evolutionary Relationship by Comparing DNA Sequences Using Cladistic Analysis

DNA Sequence Data

Gene: ADORA 3

	25	26	27	28	29	30	31	32	33	34	35	36	37	38	39	40	41	42	43	44	45	46	47	48	49	50	51
Outgroup: Opossum	A	T	G	G	A	C	T	A	C	A	T	G	G	T	C	T	T	T	T	T	C	A	G	C	T	T	T
A: Cat	A	T	G	G	A	C	T	A	C	A	T	G	G	T	C	T	A	C	T	T	C	A	G	C	T	T	C
B: Dog	A	T	G	G	A	C	T	A	C	A	T	G	G	T	C	T	A	C	T	T	C	A	G	C	T	T	C
C: Muskrat	A	T	G	G	A	C	T	A	C	A	T	G	G	T	C	T	T	C	T	T	C	A	G	C	T	T	T
D: Mink	A	T	G	G	A	C	T	A	C	A	T	G	G	T	C	T	A	C	T	T	C	A	G	C	T	T	C
E: Sheep	A	T	G	G	A	T	T	A	C	A	T	G	G	T	C	T	A	C	T	T	C	A	G	T	T	T	T
F: Pig	A	T	G	G	A	T	T	A	C	A	T	G	G	T	C	T	A	C	T	T	C	A	G	C	T	T	T

	52	53	54	55	56	57	58	59	60	61	62	63	64	65	66	67	68	69	70	71	72	73	74	75	76	77
Outgroup: Opossum	T	T	C	A	C	A	T	G	G	A	T	C	C	T	C	A	T	C	C	C	C	T	T	G	G	T
A: Cat	T	T	C	A	C	C	T	G	G	A	T	T	T	T	A	A	T	C	C	C	C	C	T	G	G	
B: Dog	T	T	C	A	C	C	T	G	G	A	T	T	T	T	A	A	T	C	C	C	C	C	T	A	G	
C: Muskrat	T	T	C	A	C	C	T	G	G	A	T	C	T	T	C	A	T	C	C	C	T	C	T	G	C	
D: Mink	T	T	C	A	C	C	T	G	G	A	T	T	T	T	A	A	T	C	C	C	C	C	T	A	A	
E: Sheep	T	T	C	A	C	T	T	G	G	A	T	T	C	T	C	A	T	T	C	C	C	C	T	A	A	
F: Pig	T	T	C	A	C	T	T	G	G	A	T	T	C	T	C	A	T	T	C	C	C	C	T	G	G	

Model the Process of Natural Selection Resulting from Predation

Student Results

Habitat Color 1	Prey Type 1	Prey Type 2	Prey Type 3
Number remaining at end of third generation			
Habitat Color 2	Prey Type 1	Prey Type 2	Prey Type 3
Number remaining at end of third generation			
Habitat Color 3	Prey Type 1	Prey Type 2	Prey Type 3
Number remaining at end of third generation			

LAB EXERCISE 9.3

Practice Applying Your Understanding of Natural Selection

Scenario 1: *Mycobacterium tuberculosis*, the bacteria that causes the disease tuberculosis, was once readily killed in infected individuals when they were treated with a course of antibiotic drugs. In recent years, however, strains of *M. tuberculosis* that are resistant to antibiotics have become prevalent in certain human populations.

Scenario 2: Giant pandas strip the low nutrient leaves off of bamboo stems before they feed on the pulpy shoot. They strip these leaves by running the shoot between their paw and what appears to be a "thumb" that extends from the lower part of the paw. However, this structure is not a thumb like ours; that is, it is not made up of finger bones. Instead, it is an enlarged version of one of the bones of the wrist and is immobile.

Scenario 3: Crayfish that live in deep caves appear very similar to crayfish that live in the open. However, cave crayfish are blind; although they produce eye stalks (places where eyes normally sit) that are identical to the eye stalks of open-living crayfish, they do not make functional eyes.

Scenario 4: The sickle-cell allele is more common in regions where malaria is a common disease. Individuals with two copies of the sickle-cell allele have sickle-cell disease and often die at a young age. However, individuals with one or two copies of the allele have a much lower rate of malaria than individuals who lack the allele.

Scenario 5: There are no warblers on the Galapagos Islands, but there are finches that act like warblers. On the mainland, finches are primarily seed-eating birds, while warblers tend to specialize on flying insects. Warbler finches on the Galapagos eat insects. Mainland finches have broad short bills for cracking seeds, while mainland warblers have longer, thin bills, adapted for "snatching" insects. Warbler finches on the Galapagos have much thinner bills than seed-eating finches, their closest relatives.

Scenario 6: Photosynthesis is the process that converts sun energy into chemical energy. The structure inside of plant cells that performs photosynthesis is called a chloroplast. Chloroplasts appear very similar to certain species of bacteria that can do photosynthesis. Chloroplasts appear to have evolved from bacteria that were engulfed, but not digested, by other cells. Chloroplasts cannot survive outside their host cell.

LAB EXERCISE 10.1

The Evolution of Reproductive Isolation

Lab set-up information

Obtain samples of *Microbotryum violaceum* strains from the following organisms:

- *Silene latifolia*, strains from United Kingdom (A1), Broadway, Virginia (A1 and A2)
- *Silene caroliniana*, North Carolina (A1)
- *Silene virginica*, Virginia (A1)
- *Paspalum paniculatum* (A1)
- *Lychnis flos-cuculi* (A1)

Currently these strains are available from Dr. Michael Hood at the University of Virginia (Michael.Hood@virginia.edu), but he is hopeful that they will be available via Carolina Biological Supply by the time the lab manual is published.

The *Microbotryum* samples from Dr. Hood will be frozen, desiccated sporidia. These should be initially cultured on Potato Dextrose Agar (available from Sigma or Fisher) at room temperature about a week before the crosses are to be performed. The day that the crosses are to be performed, the actively growing cultures are used to make sporidial suspensions in sterile deionized water.

To create sporidial suspensions, put a small fragment of the culture into 1 mL water. Use a hemacytometer to quantify the concentration of sporidia in each suspension. Make the concentrations of sporidia equal among suspensions by diluting down to approximately 2,500 sporidia per μL. The concentrations of the suspensions do not need to be exactly the same, but should be the same order of magnitude at least. The suspension should look slightly cloudy.

Crosses are plated on 1.5% water agar plates (20g agar/1L distilled water), 24 to 72 hours before the lab period. The bottom of the plate should be gridded as an eight-wedge "pie" and labeled with the codes listed on Table 10.2 in Lab Exercise 10.1.

To create each cross (for approximately 50 plates), pipette 50 μL of the focal strain (host: *Silene alba*, A1) into a microcentrifuge tube with 50 μL of the cross strain. Mix by tapping the tube. Pipette 2 μL of this mixture onto the center of the appropriately labeled pie wedge on the petri dishes.

Incubate the plates between 5° and 15°C.

LAB EXERCISE 10.3

Are Human Races Biological Races?

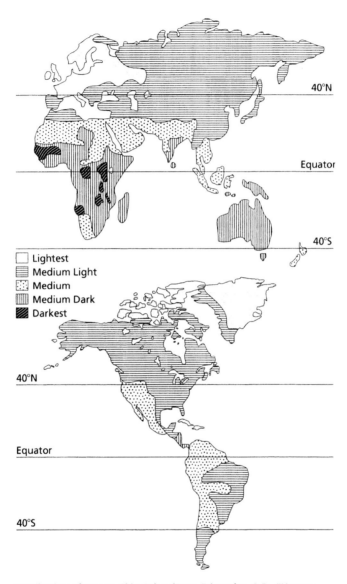

Distribution of Human Skin Color. (From Frisancho, A.R., "Human Adaption", 1979, St. Louis: The C.V. Mosby Co.; modified from Brace, C.L., and A. Montagu, "Man's Evolution", 1965, New York: Macmillan.)

The Relationship Among the Domains of Life

Woese's Tree

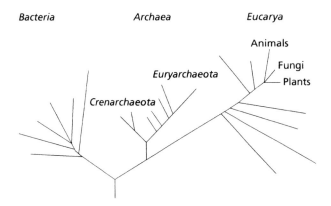

LAB EXERCISE 11.2

A Survey of the Domains Bacteria and Archaea

Alternative Gram Stain Protocol

Another alternative to the traditional Gram stain is the much simpler protocol from the American Phytopathological Society Web page, as written here:

1. Pick bacteria off plate using toothpick.
2. Transfer bacteria to microscope slide with 2–3 drops of 3% KOH. Swirl toothpick in the KOH.
3. Gram-negative bacteria will lyse in the KOH and the liquid will become viscous in 15–30 s. DNA can be lifted from the slide surface by slowly drawing up the toothpick off the slide. No viscosity will be observed in the KOH solution containing Gram-positive bacteria.

A Survey of the Kingdom Animalia

Common Animal Phyla

- **Phylum Porifera** Asymmetrical animals with no digestive tract or skeleton. Aquatic organisms that are sessile (stationary) as adults. Sponges.
- **Phylum Cnidaria** Radially symmetrical animals with incomplete digestive tracts and no skeleton. Hydra, jellyfish, sea anemones, corals.
- **Phylum Platyhelminthes** Bilaterally symmetrical animals with incomplete digestive tracts and no skeleton. Dorso-ventral flattening and a head and tail region. Marine, freshwater, terrestrial, and parasitic flatworms, planaria, tapeworms, flukes.
- **Phylum Nematoda** Bilaterally symmetrical animals with complete digestive tracts and no skeleton. Many parasites of humans and plants are members of this phylum. Roundworms.
- **Phylum Mollusca** Bilaterally symmetrical animals with complete digestive tracts, organ level specialization, and no skeleton. Most molluscs have a shell (different from an exoskeleton). Chitons, snails, slugs, clams, squids, octopus.
- **Phylum Annelida** Bilaterally symmetrical animals with complete digestive tracts and no skeleton. They have long bodies that are separated internally by partitions called septa. Segmented worms such as earthworms.
- **Phylum Arthropoda** Bilaterally symmetrical animals with complete digestive tracts. They have segmented bodies, a chitinous exoskelton (hard skeleton on the outside of their bodies), a brain, and jointed appendages (arms and legs). Insects, crabs, spiders, crustaceans (lobsters, crayfish).
- **Phylum Echinodermata** Radially symmetrical animals with complete digestive tracts and no skeleton. This marine phylum uses a unique system that makes use of water pressure for locomotion. Starfish, sea urchins, sea cucumbers.
- **Phylum Chordata** Bilaterally symmetrical animals with complete digestive tracts. This phylum contains the most advanced organisms. All have notochords (spinal cord) and an internal skeleton. All animals with backbones.

LAB EXERCISE 15.1

Sea Urchin Fertilization

Suggestions:

- Harvesting sperm and eggs requires about 50 minutes. You can perform this at the beginning of class if you want students to see the gametes, or you can perform the harvesting before class and have a few sea urchins on display.

- The procedure for spawning animals begins with the injection of 0.5M potassium chloride into the body cavity of the sea urchin using a very small gauge needle. You will need to inject 0.1–0.2 mL of KCl/inch of urchin width into both sides of the urchin. The needle should be inserted so that the KCl enters the body cavity and not the mouth.

- After injecting the sea urchin, gently shake it for a few seconds to spread the solution around. Hard shaking can kill the urchin.

- If the urchin is male, the sperm released will be milky white in color. Females will release eggs that are pale yellow to orange or maroon.

- After injection, place the male urchin mouth side down over a small Petri dish. Do not submerge the urchin. In a few minutes, white sperm will appear. Immediately collect the sperm in a pipette or eyedropper and place it into a small test tube. Store in the refrigerator (not the freezer) or on ice. Sperm will keep at 4°C for 2–5 days.

- Female urchins should be placed mouth side down on the top of a small beaker full of seawater (not submerged, but perched on the beaker). Female urchins must be in contact with sea water to shed their gametes. The shedding of gametes takes around 10–15 minutes. Try to keep the eggs and urchins at the same temperature.

- Sperm must be at the proper concentration for fertilization to occur. Too few or too many sperm decrease the odds of fertilization (polyspermy mechanisms are not 100% effective).

- Add about 50 μL of sperm to 100 mL of sea water. This is your stock solution of sperm. You might need to adjust the volume if fertilization is not occurring or if polyspermy is occurring.

- A drop of the stock solution should be enough to fertilize 5 mL of a dilute egg suspension (see the following section).

- Egg cell dilution is also necessary. Pour the eggs you harvested from the beaker into a 100-mL graduated cylinder.

- Bring the volume to 100 mL with seawater, and let the eggs settle. In the presence of sea water, the eggs will swell.

- Dilute the now swollen eggs 1:20 (that is, 10 mL of your swollen eggs into 180 mL of seawater). This is your stock solution of eggs.

LAB EXERCISE 15.4

Disease Transmission

Student Results

Source Tube Number

	1	2	3	4	5	6	7	8	9	10	11	12	13	14	15	16	17	18	19	20	21	22	23	24
1																								
2																									
3																									
4																									
+/−																									

Exchange

Each student is represented by a column. Students fill in the tube number of their exchange partner in each row and then indicate whether the test for the infectious organism was positive or negative at the end of the simulation.

Memory and Learning

Memory

Word	Number of Students Recalling Word
Apple	
Shirt	
Later	
John	
Mayor	
Green	
West	
Theory	
Planet	